LEADERSHIP ENRICHMENT SERIES

Unlimited Partnership

Building Intimacy & Teamwork
Into Your Marriage

Phil & Susy Downer   David & Teresa Ferguson

Intimacy Press
Austin, Texas

UNLIMITED PARTNERSHIP
BUILDING INTIMACY AND TEAMWORK INTO YOUR MARRIAGE

Phil and Susy Downer
David and Teresa Ferguson

All Scripture quotations, unless otherwise indicated, are taken from the Holy Bible, New International Version. Copyright 1973, 1978, 1984, by International Bible Society. Used by permission of Zondervan Publishing House. All rights reserved.

INTIMACY PRESS • P.O. Box 201808, Austin, Texas 78720-1808
1.800.881.8008 • Fax 512.795.0853 • U.K. 0.800.966.685

ISBN - 0 - 9642845 - 6 - 1

How to Use this Study Guide

Use this study guide in relationships — learning to "impart your life" to others! As we'll explore in this resource, it's through relationships with God and others that life is lived to it's full potential. As relationships are enriched, marriages, families, churches, communities and even entire cultures are positively impacted. Suggested uses for this study guide include:

Enrich your relationship with God through...

- **Daily devotions** - use one chapter each week as the focus of daily Bible study and prayer.
- **Scripture memory** - study, memorize, and meditate on key Scripture verses in the text which have been included in the "highlight" boxes.
- **Topical Bible study** - each chapter includes a topical Bible study which focuses on key scriptural truths.
- **Praise/worship** - unhurried times of reflection and meditation will be encouraged in each chapter as you pause to consider the wonder of His love.

Enrich your relationship with your spouse and others through...

- **Individual study/couple sharing** - both partners working through each chapter and then coming together for an uninterrupted time of vulnerable sharing, encouragement, accountability, and prayer.
- **Men's/women's groups** - men or women covering together the content of each chapter and the biblical perspective. Homework could be assigned to be completed with spouses at home. The group then provides week by week encouragement, accountability and prayer.
- **Couples' Classes and Seminars** - groups of any size either for week-by-week class instruction (with homework) or for seminars, retreats and conferences.
- **Couples' Groups/Mentoring** - 2-5 couples working through each chapter, first as a couple (see individual/couple sharing above) and then coming together for a time of group sharing, encouragement, accountability and prayer.

CBMC of USA

The Christian Business Men's Committee of USA (CBMC) is an interdenominational, evangelical ministry comprised of more than 50,000 men and couples involved in 1,000 committees and ministry teams nationwide.

The primary purpose of CBMC

- To present Jesus Christ as Savior and Lord to other business and professional people, and to train them to carry out Christ's Great Commission in the marketplace.

The vision statement of CBMC

- Compelled by the love of Christ and empowered by the Holy Spirit, the vision of CBMC is carried out by men, couples and families impacting the world by saturating the business and professional community with the Gospel of Jesus Christ by establishing, equipping and mobilizing teams where we work and live that yield spiritual reproducers so that one shall become a thousand (Mark 12:28-31, 2 Timothy 2:1-4, Isaiah 60:22).

Ministry opportunities in CBMC

- **Committee teams** - More than 500 teams of men meet weekly across the United States for prayer, Bible study, outreach, and discipleship.
- **Ministry teams** - Over 500 teams of men and couples meet in homes and other settings for evangelistic Bible studies and outreach dinner parties.
- **Living Proof teams** - These are groups of men and couples who meet to focus on the Biblical processes of lifestyle evangelism and discipleship
- **Small groups** - Hundreds of CBMC-sponsored couples' groups meet weekly to discuss topics ranging from principles of financial stewardship to how to build godly marriages.
- **Outreach** - CBMC sponsors more than 2,000 outreach meetings each year, presenting the truths of Jesus Christ to more than 100,000 uncommitted and unchurched people.
- **Discipleship** - Annually, more than 25,000 discipling teams are formed.
- **Conferences/Retreats** - CBMC sponsors more than 30 family, men's and couples' conferences and retreats including a National Men's Conference.
- **Leadership prayer breakfasts** - CBMC participates in about 25 community prayer breakfasts to acknowledge God's role in civic affairs and to present the gospel to civic leaders.
- **Forums** - Business owners and top executives meet monthly in small accountability groups for problem-solving and support.

CBMC of USA • 1800 McCallie Avenue, Chattanooga, TN 37404 • 800.566.2262

Intimate Life Ministries

Intimate Life Ministries is a training and resource ministry, helping build Healthy Churches for the 21st Century - churches with a Great Commandment Heart and a Great Commission Passion. Specifically, Intimate Life Ministries seeks to help restore to the church:

A Great Commandment Heart...a heart which
- enjoys intimacy with God and within marriage, family and the church,
- through experiencing biblical truth,
- because of God's provision for both our fallenness and our aloneness.

Intimate Life Ministries is Multi-Faceted

- **The Center for Marriage and Family Intimacy** (CMFI) - provides instruction and materials to assist homes, churches and cities in becoming "fortified" against enemies such as divorce, abuse, and neglect - providing places of refuge, security, and rest.
- **Galatians 6:6 Ministry** - provides special ministry to Christian leaders. Intimacy Retreats and other events, designed especially for ministry couples, are hosted in key cities throughout the United States and in other countries, offering times of restoration, renewal, and equipping.
- **Intimate Life Communications** - provides radio, television, video, and audio support to Intimate Life Ministries and participating churches.
- **Intimacy Press** - produces and distributes resources which uniquely address the intimacy message.
- **Worship Connection** - assists individuals and churches in the area of intimacy with God. Through materials, conferences, and pastor/worship leader networks, it promotes the message of genuine worship - both individually and corporately.

Intimate Life Ministries is assisted by the ministry of Professional Associates and a network of pastors, ministry leaders and trainers.

Intimate Life Ministries • P.O. Box 201808 Austin, Texas 78720-1808
1.800.881.8008 • Fax 512.795.0853 • U.K. 0.800.966.685

Acknowledgments

We would like to thank the people who invested in our lives spiritually. These disciplers include Jim and Mary Gail Lyon, Liane Day, Dave and Judi Hill, and Joe and Gladys Coggeshall (deceased). God used these friends to bring us to Himself, and to teach us to walk with Him in life and with each other in marriage.

What a tremendous blessing we have received from the godly and inspirational leadership of the Board of Directors of CBMC and the faithful and sacrificial service of the staff, members and friends who faithfully serve throughout the United States in the cause of winning and discipling business and professional men, their wives, and families.

Great thanks is due to David and Teresa Ferguson, Don McMinn and the entire staff at Intimate Life Ministries.

Finally, we would like to thank our parents, Sam and Jessie Downer (both deceased) who loved and supported us and Paul and Rena Olschner who continue to model love, faith and hope in their Christ-centered lives and marriage.

All proceeds derived from the sale of this book will be contributed to the ministries of CBMC of USA and Intimate Life Ministries.

Phil and Susy Downer
September 18, 1996

"It's not good to be alone" — and God has abundantly blessed us in this writing project, not only with co-laborers from the Intimate Life Ministry team but with those who support, encourage, and "remove aloneness." Special thanks to:

Don McMinn - gifted writer, who helped develop much of this material in his work with the Intimate Life Newsletter. He, along with the entire McMinn family — Mary, Lauren, and Sarah, spent countless hours under significant time constraints editing and assembling this resource.

Barry Metz - gifted student of the Word and talented writer who contributes significantly to the biblical content in all our work and in this case played a critical production role as well.

Julia Metz - the most talented graphic designer any team could wish for. She makes content "come alive" through her creativity and multi-faceted design talents.

This resource is as much theirs, as anyone's. Thanks team! We need to tell you more often —we love you!

Since our first encounter with the CBMC ministry, their leadership team and Phil and Susy Downer, we've been challenged and blessed by the dedication and vision of their Great Commission passion. Three special Intimate Life ministry "friends" who we've come to know through their CBMC involvement - Eddie Watkins, Bruce Maginnis and Rob Robbins - gave us great review and feedback on concepts for this study guide.

It's a true joy to join the CBMC team in seeking to further the Lord's enriching impact on marriages, families, churches and communities throughout the land.

David and Teresa Ferguson
September 18, 1996

Contents

Foreword

" If God can change him, God can do anything." Susy had caught a glimmer of hope for our marriage. Divorce had been at the back of her mind since our honeymoon, but she had postponed the decision year after year thinking it would eventually get better.

I had come to Christ after attending a Christian Business Men's Committee (CBMC) luncheon. It changed my life! Susy could see the difference. She saw the Bible "working" in my life and within a year she had embraced Christ as her Savior. God's timing couldn't have been better. But her incredible spiritual encounter did not immediately heal the wounds I had caused. Because I had hurt her so deeply, she had trouble mustering any feelings for me at all.

Perhaps you can relate to our story. Perhaps you too have a relationship with God but you are still struggling in your marriage.

In the following pages, we want to share biblical principles and personal experiences which will motivate and equip you to develop a fulfilling, intimate marriage.

The co-authors of this book are David and Teresa Ferguson, founding directors of Intimate Life Ministries. The Fergusons have a wonderful gift of presenting biblical truths regarding marriage and family in an easy-to-understand manner.

Susy and I wish we had known these biblical principles of marriage years ago - knowing them would have helped us through the quagmire and twisted wreckage of our journey. In this book, Susy and I will share parts of our journey, and the Fergusons will share the biblical principles which could have helped us avoid so much pain. Over the last several years we have studied, taught, and cried through the principles presented by the Fergusons. In turn, we have been able to share the material with other couples. We hope this book will be used of God to help you experience His abundance in your marriage.

David and Teresa's journey into marriage, like ours, started out pretty rocky. At their training conferences, they vulnerably share how hurts and pains accumulated in their marriage to the point where, seven years into marriage, laying in bed one evening, David anxiously asked Teresa, "Do you still love me?" only to hear, "David, I don't feel anything for you. I'm just numb." From this sense of hopelessness and despair, God began a miraculous work of healing, freedom, and restored intimacy in their marriage.

When we first met the Fergusons, Susy and I had a good marriage, but we still had much to learn. The Lord has used many of the principles in this book to deepen our relationship.

This book is for those who want to improve a good marriage and for those whose marriage is in trouble. The truth is, no one has "arrived"; marriage is a journey, and every step brings new challenges.

In this book we'll address some of the following key issues:

1. Becoming "best friends." In marriage, partners share a lot in common - a last name, children, and sometimes even a church pew! But that doesn't necessarily mean we're friends. In the Bible, David and Jonathan had a healthy bond of friendship which transcended business, financial and family pressures. How can we develop the friendship aspect of our marriage?

2. Living vulnerably. Joshua, after his defeat at Ai, was willing to cry out to the Lord in pain, defeat, embarrassment, and uncertainty, and do it in front of his team! Why can't we be honest with our spouse and share the deep issues with which we are struggling?

3. Ministry teamwork. Aquilla and Priscilla lived, worked, and ministered together as a team. How can we, in our marriages, operate as a unit - complementing one another's gifts, standing in the gap for one another's weaknesses, and multiplying our productivity, effectiveness and faithfulness?

4. Great sex in marriage! How can the physical relationship with our partner be the fulfilling and rewarding union God meant it to be?

This book is a workbook! You will be asked to fill in the blanks, pause to discuss certain issues, and share vulnerably with another person. It may seem uncomfortable at first, but remember - time does not automatically eradicate problems and pain—constructive talk can. Each chapter includes a Biblical Perspective, Experiencing Biblical Truth exercise and Intimacy Praxis. These exercises will challenge your marriage to deeper levels of intimacy, whether used in individual study, men's groups or couples' groups.

Our prayer is that the Lord will bless and prosper His word in your life and marriage!

> Phil and Susy Downer
> *President*, **Christian Business Men's Committee of U.S.A.**
> David and Teresa Ferguson
> *Director*, **Intimate Life Ministries**

Intimacy — Antidote For Aloneness

Phil and Susy's Journey

"I really feel that I have been defrauded. You're not the man I dated and you're not the man I agreed to marry." Susy's words hit me like a brick. It was the second night of our honeymoon and Susy had concluded that she "made a mistake" in marrying me. During our months of dating, I developed a love for Susy beyond anything I'd ever known, and I did my best to win her love and affection. It's not that I hid who I was, it's just that no one really knew who I was. I probably didn't even know myself. What I did know was that I was "damaged merchandise" marrying a woman who had never been yelled at before. No wonder Susy was shocked, disappointed and...alone.

My angry spirit that erupted on our honeymoon was born years earlier on the driveway of the house where I grew up. My father had just introduced me to his new girlfriend and her two snobby children whom, I was told, were soon to become my brother and sister. I loved my mother, so I deeply resented this "intruder" who was invading our home. It hurt me to see mother wounded so badly. Twice, she even attempted suicide.

My reaction to this hurtful experience? My innermost thought was, "I'll never hug my dad again, nor will I ever cry; from now on it's, 'Don't let people get too close.'" That was my adaptation of the great American axiom for men— "Big boys don't cry." That day, as a young boy, I made some decisions that would shape my concept of life and relationships - and adversely affect my marriage from day one. That day, I decided to face life...emotionally alone!

Both Susy and I were raised to be very independent. Her "dogged independence" and my "it's me against the world" approach to life left us feeling very much alone—even though we were married.

Our relationship had a rough beginning, but now, after 25 years of marriage and six wonderful children, Susy and I are overwhelmed with the joy of being partners, co-laborers, best friends, lovers and joint heirs in Christ! Through our relationship with Christ, His Word, and one another, the Lord has healed our marriage.

David and Teresa's Reflections

In our teaching of biblical principles of marriage and family, Teresa and I usually take couples all the way back to the story of creation. Here we see God "setting up" the universe, and we read about God's initial thoughts about marriage.

The first principle we see in Genesis, regarding building intimacy and teamwork into your marriage, has to do with the "aloneness" factor.

Buried two-thirds of the way through Genesis 2, God makes a startling declaration—"It is not good for man to be alone." God's declaration is startling because although Adam had a perfect relationship with God, he still declared that Adam was "alone." Adam's *spiritual* aloneness had been removed through his intimate walk with the Creator, but even with a perfect relationship with God, something was lacking. Adam was needy. God proceeded to provide for man's aloneness with the creation of Eve, a helpmate suitable for him. Lest we overlook it, the first stated purpose of marriage was to remove aloneness.

> *...the first stated purpose of marriage was to remove aloneness.*

But in Genesis 3, Adam and Eve, in a fatal moment and with a single choice, chose sin and Satan rather than God and his provision. Needy by creation, now Adam and Eve were fallen by choice. Their fall brought the return of spiritual and interpersonal "aloneness" and they experienced shame, fear and nakedness. Just as God had provided for man's aloneness, He now provided for his fallenness. He slew an animal and used it as a covering. Provision for their "fallenness" came as blood was shed, typifying the *"Lamb that was slain from the creation of the world"* (Revelation 13:8). In the dawn of creation, Adam and Eve had two problems, aloneness and fallenness, and God lovingly made provision for both.

We, as descendants of Adam, are in a similar position; we are born needful of relationships with God and others, and we are fallen by nature and by choice. From Genesis to Revelation, the Bible speaks of God's "scarlet thread of redemption" which has lovingly made provision for both our aloneness and our fallenness.

God could have addressed our problems from a distance; He could have simply spoken the solution just like He spoke the worlds into existence. But beginning in Genesis 2, God personally entered the Garden to address Adam's needs, and 2,000 years ago, the Word became flesh in the person of Jesus to fulfill the ultimate payment for man's sin and reestablish the possibility of fallen man's intimate relationship with a holy God.

Across the pages of scripture, why did God choose to become personally involved in solving man's dilemma? Why did Christ spend so much time with His disciples? Why did He commend Mary for choosing to sit at His feet rather than be busy (Luke 10:38-42)? Why, after the resurrection, did Jesus take time to eat dinner with the disciples? As we study the life of Jesus, one truth is obvious - He placed a high priority on relationships! He was concerned with man's aloneness. But God's concern did not stop there.

At the cross, our sins were paid for and forgiveness became available— but why? One critical reason was that mankind could once again have a relationship with God. The death of Christ on the cross was necessary because we were separated from God by our sins, and the cross provided the bridge back to God. Because of the cross, access to God was now open and as recipients of divine grace, believers could boldly approach God's throne.

But the cross not only addressed our fallenness, it also spoke to our aloneness: *"And I no longer live but Christ lives in me"* (Galatians 2:20); He has come to take up His abode in us (John 15:4); He has also placed us into His body, the church, so that when one hurts, we all hurt and when one rejoices, we all rejoice (1 Corinthians 12). Before the cross, we were either Jew or Gentile and there was no basis for closeness or unity between the two groups, no real resources for breaking down dividing walls. But in Christ, we were made one and He is the head over us all. *"For He, Himself, is our peace, who made both groups into one, and broke down the barrier of the dividing wall, by abolishing in His flesh the enmity... so that you are no longer strangers and aliens, but you are fellow citizens with the saints"* (Ephesians 2:14,19).

Yes, God is committed to remove our aloneness, and He does so through relationships—*intimate relationships*. He provided Jesus Christ, through whom our sense of spiritual aloneness can be removed, and He has given us three other divine relationships - marriage, family, and the church - through which our sense of interpersonal aloneness can be removed.

Experience teaches us that shallow, surface relationships will not remove aloneness. It's possible to be married and still feel alone; it's possible to be around people all day long and still feel lonely. That's why we say that only intimate relationships are the antidote for aloneness because intimacy involves a deep mutual "knowing" for the purpose of caring involvement.

As we explore God's design for intimacy, we'll discover some potentials (like becoming one in spirit, soul, and body) and some hindrances (like the unhealed hurt that Phil and Susy experienced on their honeymoon and the baggage from childhood that Phil carried into their marriage).

It's time to check your "intimacy" vital signs:

- Do you ever feel disconnected, distant, withdrawn, alone in your marriage (the secular world often calls this incompatibility)?
- Would you describe your relationship with your children as intimate?
- Can you name three friends who know you deeply and with whom you are open and vulnerable?

On the following pages we begin our journey - our pursuit of intimacy!

What is man that Thou art mindful of Him?

God declared in Genesis 2:18, *"It is not good for man to be alone."* To experience God's intended abundance in life, marriage, family and community, this "aloneness" factor must be addressed. How could Adam have a perfect relationship with God and still be alone? Where does "aloneness" come from?

Aloneness is related to how God created us needing relationships with Himself and with others. There is a spiritual and interpersonal dimension to aloneness which can be described in terms of "vertical" and "horizontal." One can have a relationship with God (vertical) and not be spiritually alone but still be "interpersonally" alone (horizontal). It could be said, therefore, that Adam was alone interpersonally, but not alone spiritually. After the fall, however, this changed. After Genesis 3, everyone entered the world both spiritually and interpersonally "alone." And this aloneness is resolved through intimate relationships with God and others.

> *How could Adam have a perfect relationship with God and still be alone?*

Study Questions

Reflect on your need for intimate relationships with God and others: In what ways does God make Himself available to you?

_____

_____

What human relationships has He given you through which He might remove your interpersonal aloneness?

_____

_____

Aloneness is always a relational issue. Spiritual aloneness is answered by a relationship with God. In Genesis 3, God sought for Adam, seeking to restore the broken relationship. Throughout the Old Testament, God resided in the tabernacle or temple with His people. In the New Testament, Jesus appeared as Emmanuel, "God With Us." As Jesus' ministry was coming to an end, He promised the disciples in the Upper Room that He would not leave them as "orphans," but would give them another Helper who would be with them and abide with them forever. He promised that even though He was going away, they would not be left alone. The Holy Spirit was given not just to teach and convict of sin, but to be with us, to remove our spiritual aloneness. Jesus reiterated this in the Great Commission, *"I am with you always"* (Matthew 28:20).

> *What is salvation? What is eternal life? It is the intimate knowing, the intimate experiencing of God forever (John 17:3).*

What is salvation? What is eternal life? It is the intimate knowing, the intimate experiencing of God forever (John 17:3). The moment of new birth is our first experience of no longer being alone spiritually. Our spiritual aloneness is additionally addressed by God as the Spirit comforts in difficulty, illumines the Word of God for personal application, and convicts of sin. When we face judgment *("Just as man is destined to die once, and after that to face judgment"* Hebrews 9:27), Jesus the Judge will come alongside as the "advocate" — we will not face judgment alone.

Study Question

Think back to the time when you made your personal commitment to Christ. Describe in what ways you came to "know" Him more intimately? In what ways were you less alone?

_____

_____

If you haven't yet made this commitment, seek out your group leader, a pastor or Christian friend to help you.

The other dimension of aloneness is an interpersonal one. No amount of education, motivation or good intentions can remove this dimension of aloneness. In families, no amount of activity, tradition or discipline can remove it. Within the church, no amount of doctrine, programming or preaching can remove it. In our culture, no amount of activism, social programming, or civic involvement can remove it. Only interpersonal relationships can satisfy man's horizontal neediness and remove this dimension of aloneness. God has made ample provision for this aspect of our neediness by providing marriage, family and the church.

We were created with a need to have relationships with both God and others. God, in His goodness, has provided for both needs. Therefore, abundant provision has been made for our aloneness.

Study Questions

As you reflect on God's provision of Himself, His Spirit, His Son and His word—just for you, that you might never be alone, how are you affected emotionally?

_____

_____

Experiencing biblical truth leads us into intimacy with God and others.

As you reflect on God's provision of your spouse, children, family, and friends—just for you, that your life might be abundantly blessed, how are you affected emotionally?

_____

_____

_____

How might this stirring of gratefulness in your heart prompt your sensitive care and giving toward God and others?

_____

_____

_____

Experiencing Biblical Truth— Why It's Important

Accoding to British demographer David Barrett, more than 7,600 people leave the church every day in North America and Europe- "converts to other religions or to irreligion." In other words, one would have to plant almost 8 churches of 1,000 or more people every day of the year to offset the number of people walking away from churches already in existence.

Why do people leave churches? William Hendricks, author of *Exit Interviews, Revealing Stories of Why People are Leaving the Church,* listed the number one reason as: people no longer evaluate Christianity on the basis of whether it is true, but how it is true in their own lives. The question today is not whether God exists, but what difference does God make?

Recent studies indicate that 78% of new church attenders are seeking ways to strengthen family relationships, but 73% come to believe the church is not relevant to their lives.

Relationships and Relevance

Churches who reach people in the 21st century must understand these two terms: relationships and relevance.

People are not merely searching for truth - they're searching for how truth can be applied to their lives. They're wanting to experience biblical truth.

An integral part of the *Intimate Life* message involves a conviction that we must *experience* biblical truth. It's the experiencing of biblical truth that leads us into intimacy with God and with others. As we truly experience biblical truth, we move beyond merely obeying "rules and regulations" and come to enjoy the blessing of intimate relationships. This proposition, if taken seriously, will challenge many current teaching paradigms. As believers, we'll focus not only on hearing the truth but experiencing it. As Christian leaders and teachers, we'll no longer be satisfied with merely imparting spiritual truth in a relevant manner, but we'll see the necessity of having people experience what they're learning - right in their own marriages! families! and friendships!

Couple or Group Activity: Have each spouse or group member select three of the "one anothers" listed below that they would most like to see "more of" at home. After sharing together and prayer, make it a goal over the next month to consciously experience these "one anothers" in your home and group.

- Love one another (John 13:34).
- Depend on one another (Romans 12:5 AMP).
- Be devoted to one another (Romans 12:10).
- Out-do one another in showing honor (Romans 12:10).
- Rejoice with one another (Romans 12:15, 1 Corinthians 12:26).
- Weep with one another (Romans 12:15).
- Be of the same mind toward one another (Romans 12:16).
- Don't judge one another (Romans 14:13).
- Receive one another (Romans 15:7).
- Admonish one another (Romans 15:14).
- Greet one another (Romans 16:16).
- Wait for one another (1 Corinthians 11:33).
- Care for one another (1 Corinthians 12:25).
- Serve one another (Galatians 5:13).
- Be kind to one another (Ephesians 4:32).
- Forgive one another (Ephesians 4:32, Colossians 3:13).
- Be tenderhearted toward one another (Ephesians 4:42).
- Encourage one another (1 Thessalonians 5:11).
- Submit to one another (Ephesians 5:21).
- Forbear with one another (Ephesians 4:2, Colossians 3:13).
- Stimulate love in one another (Hebrews 10:24).
- Show hospitality one to another (1 Peter 5:5).
- Minister gifts one to another (1 Peter 4:10).
- Be clothed in humility one toward another (1 Peter 5:5).
- Don't speak evil against one another (James 4:11).
- Don't grumble against one another (James 5:9).
- Confess your faults one to another (James 5:16).
- Pray for one another (James 5:16).
- Fellowship with one another (1 John 1:7).
- Don't be puffed up against one another (1 Corinthians 4:6).
- Bear one another's burdens (Galatians 6:2).

Accountability note: Encourage one another unto love and good deeds (Hebrews 10:24) as you check up on each group member.

Childhood Questionnaire

It's impossible to be intimate with someone you don't know. A great way to truly "know" another person is to explore together your growing up experiences. Friends develop a much deeper understanding of one another and marriage partners begin to see additional ways in which they must "leave" their family of origin. Complete the following inventory and then share together with your spouse or group members.

1. How did you know your parents loved each other as you were growing up? How did they show it? (For instance: they hugged and kissed a lot, they spoke kindly to each other, they laughed a lot together.)

   _____

   _____

2. Indicate either **mom**, **dad, both**, or **neither** next to the following phrases to help describe your home life as a child.

   Family leader -

   Main disciplinarian -

   Quick temper -

   Comfortable giving affection to me -

   Hard to please -

Parent I felt closest to -

3. How did mom and dad handle conflict with you?

    Dad would-

    Mom would-

4. Check any of the following phrases that seem to describe remembrances about your childhood:

    ☐ Our family appeared as normal to everyone else – but wasn't.
    ☐ I was cared about because of the things I did – my performance.
    ☐ I was loved for who I was – my character.
    ☐ I felt like an outsider, an observer of the rest of the family.
    ☐ Our home was demanding, performance – based, lots of rules.
    ☐ I often felt alone.
    ☐ I always felt like we "walked on eggshells" around our house.
    ☐ I seemed to always be the "adult," even when my parents were around.
    ☐ It was always extremely important for me to please everyone.

5. Now that you're an adult and have observed families, what do you think was possibly missing in yours? (For example, "I realize now my mom was overly controlling. My parents didn't make me feel very secure. We could have used a lot more joy and laughter around my house.")

    _____

    _____

6. Do you think some of your experiences as a child may be neg-
   atively affecting how you relate to your spouse? In what
   ways? (For instance, "I resist my wife's suggestions because
   they remind me of my controlling mother." "I need a lot of
   my husband's attention because I didn't get it from my dad.")

   _____

   _____

   _____

7. How did you feel as you were completing the above questions?

   _____

   _____

   _____

8. When you have finished this exercise, be sure to set aside
   plenty of time to discuss your responses with your spouse.
   Listen carefully and responsively to all that your partner says.
   Share comforting words, pray together for God's freedom and
   peace, and then discuss contributions each of you could make
   toward enriching your marriage.

   _____

   _____

   _____

Chapter Two

Exploring Deeper Intimacy Needs

Intimacy Means More Than Sex

Phil and Susy's Journey

Before I married Phil, I knew he had been with other women, but I was sure of his love for and devotion to me and assumed our physical relationship after marriage would be wonderful and fulfilling. However, on the second night of our honeymoon, Phil became irritated and frustrated and then took his wrath out on me with a barrage of accusations and criticisms. I had never heard such uncontrollable anger; in fact I was 21 years old and had never even been yelled at. Now I was married to a "screamer." I cried myself to sleep that night wondering, "Who is this man I married? Certainly not the man I fell in love with."

One of the hardest aspects of dealing with Phil's anger was not only the pain it caused me, but his expectation that after he "blew his stack," the appropriate way to heal the hurt was to be physically intimate. I didn't refuse, but on the inside I was resentful and hurt. From that day forward, I had to live with the uncertainty of not knowing when Phil would turn on me as though I were his enemy.

When we first got married, I really loved Susy with all my heart. But I just couldn't get along with her. The truth was, I had a hard time getting along with anyone for very long in any type of close relationship. In Viet Nam, my friend and fellow machine-gunner, Ralph, described me as more dangerous than the North Vietnamese army when I got angry. Growing up, my mother told me that she was never allowed to express emotion, therefore she encouraged me to express mine—any way I wanted.

Even after Susy and I became Christians, we probably would have divorced had it not been for some caring friends in the Christian community who discipled us. We affectionately call them our "safety net." A doctor named Jim met with me for almost three years as we studied the "Operation Timothy" books (a discipleship course produced by CBMC). A women named Liane met with Susy for a year using the same study. Then Jim and his wife Mary Gail met with us as a couple every week for three years. Through that time of discipleship we saw first-hand, how Christians deal with relational issues and how we could grow in Christ. Through their example and the teaching of Scripture, we began the long process of analyzing our differences and the pain we had inflicted on each other.

During our discipleship time we studied and memorized key Bible passages dealing with marriage such as Ephesians 4:26, 27, and 29 and Ephesians 5:21, 25, and 29. Sometimes our experience with Scripture was merely an intellectual one. We had truth in our heads but all together, it was not affecting our walk. For instance, James 5:16 says, *"Therefore confess your sins to each other and pray for each other so that you may be healed."* It's amazing how many times men have confessed to me bad attitudes, conduct, and abusive behavior toward their wives, but when I told them that they needed to tell their wives the things they were telling me, they actually looked surprised. There's a difference between intellectually "knowing" truth and actually experiencing it.

Perhaps the most significant way in which I have learned to experience biblical truth is in the area of intimacy needs. Through our exposure to Intimate Life Ministries we have learned that just as God created us with physical needs such as air, food and water, He also created us with intimacy needs.

I'll let David and Teresa explain.

David and Teresa's Reflections

In order to rebuild broken relationships and to live together peaceably, we must understand the ten commonly identified intimacy needs.

Each of us has unique and special relational needs which, when met, produce the experience and "feelings" of being loved. It's important not only to *know* that I'm loved mentally but also to *experience* it emotionally and behaviorally. The emotional feelings of love are very often, for example, related to needs for attention, affection and appreciation being met. Understanding an individual's significant relational needs helps equip us to better love this person as we play a role in helping meet some of these needs. As a back-drop for better understanding this relationship between love and needs, we first need to review God's love for us.

God Meets Needs!

"*God demonstrated his love toward us...*" (Romans 5:8). It's this demonstration of love that is meaningful. God doesn't simply "verbalize" His love...He demonstrates it. One meaningful way to better understand this demonstration of love is to view God's role in meeting your needs. There's a need for forgiveness which is met in Christ's death. There are needs for acceptance and for renewed purpose which are met in Christ. The needs for cleansing, strength, discernment and guidance are met through Christ's gift of the Holy Spirit. On and on we could go but the key realization is this..."How do I know and experience God's love for me?" He has met and continues to meet, my needs!

Whether you realize it or not, two significant truths are at work in your relationships. These truths are either working "for" you or "against" you.

Basic Needs Met = Fulfillment

Relationships such as marriage and family have identifiable "basic" needs which, when met, produce a sense of abundance, joy and fulfillment. Some of these basic needs are easily identified while others are "discovered" by trial and error. Needing to feel secure in marriage fidelity for example, is an easily identified need. The need to be appreciated for contributions to our family and for character strengths might be less obvious...and thus discovered after a family member "explodes" after feeling unimportant, taken-for-granted and used! A marriage with an abundance of "met" needs will experience abundance, retain romance and be better protected from temptations. A family which focuses on giving to meet one another's needs will experience closeness, affirm each other's value, and serve as a powerful example to a self-centered world.

Basic Needs Unmet = Frustration

You have a basic physical need for sleep and when it goes unmet you feel uptight, irritable and easily frustrated. It's the same with basic relational needs. A marriage partner who goes for long periods without attention, affection or appreciation can easily become vulnerable to moodiness, retaliation or rejection.

A child who misses out on attention, acceptance or affirmation can begin to "act out" in order to gain attention or strike out against those who withhold such basic needs.

God created us with these intimacy needs. For instance, we all seem to have the need for: attention, acceptance, appreciation, support, encouragement, affection, approval, security, comfort, and respect. To recognize these needs is not a sign of weakness but rather an acceptance of how God made us and how we can and should minister to one another.

These intimacy needs are: cross cultural (Asians, Africans, Anglos - all nationalities have these needs), life-long (needs don't diminish with age or maturity - a senior adult has the same needs as a child), and continuous (needs can never be met "once-for-all," they must constantly be met). God has promised to meet our needs (Philippians 4:19). He often chooses to meet our needs through other people and He desires to involve us in giving to the needs of others!

Here's a list of key intimacy needs and biblical references which encourage our giving to one another:

- **Attention** - To take thought of another and convey appropriate interest, concern, and support; to enter into another's world. *"But that the members (of the body) should have the same care for one another"* (1 Corinthians 12:25).

- **Acceptance** - Deliberate and ready reception with a favorable response; to receive willingly; to regard as good and proper. *"Wherefore accept one another, just as Christ also accepted us to the glory of God"* (Romans 15:7).

- **Appreciation** - To recognize with gratitude; to communicate with words and feelings, personal gratefulness for another person; to praise. *"I praise you..."* (1 Corinthians 11:2).

- **Support/Bear Burden** - To come alongside and gently help carry a burden; to assist in a struggle or problem; to provide for. *"Carry each other's burdens, and in this way you will fulfill the law of Christ"* (Galatians 6:2).

- **Encouragement** - To urge forward and positively persuade toward a goal; to inspire with courage, spirit, or hope; to stimulate. *"Therefore encourage one another and build each other up"* (1 Thessalonians 5:11).

- **Affection** - To communicate care and closeness through physical touch and affirming words. *"Greet one another with a holy kiss"* (Romans 16:16).

- **Respect** - To value and regard highly; to convey great worth; to esteem. *"Show proper respect to everyone"* (1 Peter 2:17).

- **Security** - Freedom from exposure to danger; to put beyond hazard of losing, want, or deprivation; confidence of "harmony" in relationships. *"May those who love You be secure"* (Psalm 122:6).

- **Comfort** - To give strength and hope to; to ease grief or trouble; to console, cheer. *"The God of all comfort, who comforts us in all our troubles, so that we can comfort those in any trouble"* (2 Corinthians 1:3,4).

- **Approval** - To accept as satisfactory; to give formal or official sanction to; to have or express a favorable opinion; to approve of. *"Because anyone who serves Christ in this way is pleasing to God and approved by men"* (Romans 14:18).

Pause and reflect on which three of these needs you might most enjoy receiving from your spouse, and then guess which three your spouse might most enjoy receiving from you. At the end of the chapter we'll work together on these exercises.

Phil and Susy's Journey

As we studied these intimacy needs, we began to understand how different we were. For example, Susy and I both need appreciation, but the specific way we like to receive it is different. Susy feels appreciated when I do something nice for her; I feel appreciated when she refrains from correcting me in public while I'm talking. Likewise, we both want to respect each other and be respected. Susy feels respected when I listen to her advice, even if I don't take it. I feel respected when she takes my advice (when we both agree that it's right).

We both need approval, but because of my insecure background, I need to hear it more often and even at a higher volume!

David and Teresa's Reflections

Pause and take a minute to write out an example of what each of these ten needs might "look like" to you in your marriage:

I sense my partner's:
- attention when _____
- acceptance when _____
- appreciation when _____
- support when _____
- encouragement when _____
- affection when _____
- respect when _____
- security when _____
- comfort when _____
- approval when _____

Phil and Susy's Journey

As I was working through the material on "Intimacy Needs," I realized that these needs—met or unmet—greatly influence the sexual aspect of the marriage relationship. When we were first married, I was totally ignorant as to the wonderful way that God had "wired" our wives relative to their physical desire for a woman, emotional intimacy and physical intimacy are intricately entwined.

Another way that needs and the physical relationship are related is the whole area of guarding one's heart and mind. It is very difficult, if not impossible, for a man to meet any of the ten intimacy needs of his wife if he struggles with impure thoughts and activities, because our thought life is known by the Lord, and sin hinders our fellowship with God and the ones we love. Also, our wives intuitively know that things are not right, even if they don't know for sure what we're thinking. Here are some suggestions for how men can protect their minds and hearts in the area of sexual sin. Susy also has corresponding suggestions for women.

Phil's List

1. Scripture is clear that the eye is the gateway to the heart, so many years ago I made a covenant with my eyes similar to what Job did, *"I made a covenant with my eyes not to look lustfully at a girl"* (Job 31:1). I purposed that I would not look at anything or anyone that would defile, hamper, or discourage my relationship with the Lord or my relationship with my wife. When I stay in hotel rooms, before unpacking my suitcase, I pray over the room and quote Colossians 3:5-9, *"Put to death, therefore, whatever belongs to your earthly nature: sexual immorality, impurity, lust, evil desires and greed, which is idolatry. Because of these, the wrath of God is coming. You used to walk in these ways, in the life you once lived. But now you must rid yourselves of all such things as these: anger, rage, malice, slander, and filthy language from your lips."*

2. One of the reasons some men fall into sexual sin is that they counsel women. It's dangerous for a man to allow a woman to share intimate subjects with him such as problems, hurts, and pains. Women should counsel women. Men should counsel men.

3. I have several accountability groups that I meet with for different areas of my life, and in each one I ask the men to examine my life with respect to my commitment to purity. One of these groups is extremely aggressive - it spends a lot of time questioning each man over every aspect of his life. It's hard to hide from men who get to know you this well and spend so much time sifting through your life.

4. Because I have made this covenant with my eyes and ears, my entire focus and desire is on Susy and no one else. This is God's intention - that we be focused only on our wives. Because of this singular focus, I find increasingly that while Susy may not have the same youthful look she did at 20 years of age and before six children, she is still the most exciting, appealing, attractive, sexy woman I know.

Susy's List

1. As a woman, I'll never fully understand the visual attraction

men have for women. I know that God made men this way so I want to help Phil avoid things that could cause him and our sons, Paul, Matt, and Josh, to stumble. For example, Phil told me that some things that I received in the mail, most of which came unsolicited, were sources of temptation. I finally had to request that they take our names off their mailing list. I even try to get the underwear catalogues out of the mail before the men of our house might be tempted to look at them.

2. Often Phil would mention how he took a deliberate step to avoid a situation that could be misunderstood, such as going to a woman's room during a convention to retrieve his brief case. I appreciate his caution and try to compliment and encourage him for taking such precautions. Many women do not understand the depth of pressure and the pervasiveness of temptation that the world offers to our husbands.

3. I have wonderful sisters in Christ to whom I am accountable and have always wanted Phil to be involved in accountability groups as well. I encourage these times and do not resent the time he's away from the family during these meetings. He always tries to be sensitive and considerate relative to the timing and duration.

4. When we eat at a restaurant, I appreciate the fact that Phil wants me to sit in the chair facing the room and he sits in the chair facing the wall, just so he'll not be distracted. This really makes me feel respected, loved and accepted.

David and Teresa's Reflections

It's time for another quiz:

- How well do you know your spouse's most important needs?
- How do these needs when they are met or unmet, affect your physical relationship?
- What hindrances often plague your pursuit of intimacy?

The following exercises will help you answer these questions.

Intimate relationships - they must be developed and protected.

Intimacy doesn't just "happen"; it takes conscientious effort to develop close, meaningful relationships. And once intimacy is established, it must be protected. This twofold emphasis is seen in John 10:10, *"The thief comes only to steal and kill and destroy* (Satan wants to destroy the closeness we have with God and others); *I have come that they may have life, and have it to the full"* (one of the ways we experience a meaningful life is through intimacy with God and others).

Intimacy can be developed through:
- Affectionate Caring - "I care about you."
- Vulnerable Communication - "I trust you."
- Joint Accomplishment - "I need you."
- Mutual Giving - "I love you."

Intimacy must be protected from:
- Emotional bondage (hinders affectionate caring)
- Fear (hinders vulnerable communication)
- Self-sufficiency (hinders joint accomplishment)
- Selfishness (hinders mutual giving)

Let's take a closer look at these common hindrances to intimacy.

> *"Get rid of all bitterness, rage and anger... Be kind and compassionate to one another, forgiving each other, just as in Christ God forgave you"*
>
> *(Ephesians 4:31, 32).*

Affectionate Caring Hindered by Emotional Bondage

It's difficult, if not impossible, to have a caring, loving spirit if you're filled with bitterness, guilt, rage and anger. And these emotions/sins will damage all of your relationships, not just the ones to which the anger is directed. For instance, if you're angry with your boss, that anger will not only affect that relationship but it will adversely affect your relationship with your spouse, children, and friends. Anger poisons the soul.

Ephesians 4:31-32 teaches us that we must "get rid of" these vices (turn loose of, put away, empty out). This is done through forgiveness. Past hurts, even those suffered in childhood, must be properly dealt with in order to gain emotional freedom. Then we'll be free to be "kind and compassionate," and be able to engage in affectionate caring.

The guilt I feel over my un-Christlike actions can be resolved through proper confession (1 John 1:9, James 5:16).

Study Questions

At times I find myself holding onto anger concerning…

_____

_____

At times I sense conviction of my guilt concerning…

_____

_____

Vulnerable Communication Hindered by Fear

Various manifestations of fear will hinder vulnerable communication:

- If I fear your criticism or rejection, I'll hold back from sharing my feelings, hurts, or needs.
- If I fear my own inadequacy, I'll hesitate to take initiative and avoid emotionally challenging conversations.
- If I fear being hurt, disappointed, or used, I may seek to control all situations so as not to appear vulnerable or needy.
- If I question your sincerity, genuineness, or commitment, I may demand to have it "proven" before I can accept it.

"There is no fear in love, but perfect love drives out fear" (1 John 4:18).

As we begin to understand and experience the perfect love of God, our personal fears are eliminated and we're able to vulnerably relate to God. As we learn to apply His perfect love in human relationships, these relationships mature, trust develops, and vulnerability deepens.

At times I sense anxiety or fear concerning...

_____

_____

Joint Accomplishment Hindered by Self-Sufficiency

A "Maverick, Lone Ranger" mentality is damaging to every relationship. If I think I can make it on my own, why do I need you?

The truth is, we need each other! God created us to be mutually giving to each other. Practically speaking, no one person has all the gifts, talents, skills, and resources needed to get the job done.

Self-sufficiency often develops through prolonged periods of unmet needs and the associated hurt which drives a person to deny their needs or to turn to self-nurturing ways to meet them (eating, fantasizing, achievement, perfectionism and other forms of escape). Self-sufficiency is also re-enforced by the "stoic, macho, hero" mentality which is often encouraged in our society.

To the contrary, when we look to one another and say, "I need you; I can't do this without you," or "We did it - together!" - intimacy deepens.

> *"I am rich; I have acquired wealth and do not need a thing"* (Revelation 3:17).
>
> *"Apart from Me you can do nothing"* (John 15:5).

I am tempted to become self-sufficient and self-reliant when ...

_____

_____

I handle it by...

_____

_____

Mutual Giving Hindered by Selfishness

Unfortunately, we often get so obsessed with our own needs that we neglect giving to the needs of others and we begin to "take" to have our needs met. Many relationships can be characterized by a take/take mentality, but there's no satisfaction in taking to have our needs met (there's a big difference between "taking" a hug and being lovingly "given" one). A relationship characterized by taking will soon show signs of resentment, discouragement, and distance. A relationship characterized by mutual giving will be satisfying, abundant, and intimate.

> *"Do nothing out of selfish ambition or vain conceit, but in humility consider others better than yourselves"*
> *(Philippians 2:3).*

I find myself selfishly "taking" at times concerning...

_____

_____

Take a quick check of your "relational vital signs." Do you have unresolved emotional baggage? Are you hindered by fear? Are you self-sufficient or selfish? To whatever degree these hindrances have crept into your life, they will adversely affect your ability to closely relate to others. Discuss these issues with your spouse or close friend.

Top 10 Intimacy Needs

Look over this list of ten intimacy needs. First, mark the three (3) needs you consider the most important for you to receive from your spouse. Next, mark the three (3) needs you think your spouse would consider most important to receive from you.

Myself   *My Spouse*

☐   **Acceptance** - deliberate and ready reception with a favorable positive response (Romans 15:7).   ☐

☐   **Affection** - to communicate care and closeness through physical touch and affirming words (Romans 16:16).   ☐

☐   **Appreciation** - to communicate with words and feelings a personal gratefulness for another (1 Corinthians 11:2).   ☐

☐   **Approval** - expressed commendation; to think and speak well of (Romans 14:18).   ☐

☐   **Attention** - to take thought of another and convey appropriate interest and support; to enter into another's world (1 Corinthians 12:25).   ☐

☐   **Comfort** (empathy) - to come alongside with word, feeling and touch; to give consolation with tenderness (Romans 12:15).   ☐

☐   **Encouragement** - to urge forward and positively persuade toward a goal (1 Thessalonians 5:11, Hebrews 10:24).   ☐

☐   **Respect** - to value and regard highly; to convey great worth (Romans 12:10).   ☐

☐   **Security** - confidence of harmony in relationships; free from harm (Romans 12:16a).   ☐

☐   **Support** - come alongside and gently help carry a load (Galatians 6:2).   ☐

First, compare your "top three" with your spouse's "top three." How many are the same (3, 2, 1, 0)? It's not uncommon to have only "1" or "0" the same; therefore we're often tempted to give to our spouse, not what he or she needs, but what we need!

Discuss with your spouse why you chose the three you chose for yourself. In this sharing time, don't criticize your spouse.

How well did you do in selecting your partner's top three?

How could you specifically meet one or two of your partner's top three needs this week?

Enhancing Sexual Intimacy

The writer of Hebrews exhorts us that, *" the marriage bed (should be) kept pure"* (Hebrews 13:4). The best way to preserve the sanctity of the marriage bed is to maintain a vital and satisfying sexual relationship. Here are three suggestions for keeping the "sizzle" in your sex life.

Increased Sexual Desire

Sex is not all in your head, but a great deal of it is! Many couples enhance the "passion" dimension by letting their minds begin to wander over pleasurable thoughts of their spouse; maybe beginning in the morning after a tender and affectionate parting, during an afternoon bubble bath or during a relaxed reading of *Solomon on Sex* (Dillow, 1977).

A balanced relationship will also include touch in three ways:

- **Spiritual Touching** - Holding hands to pray communicates common spiritual agreement; touch in church; embrace one another at times of great joy; hold hands as a family at the dinner prayer.

- **Soul Touching** - Embrace one another as you depart and as you re-unite. Go for a walk holding hands; walk arm in arm through the mall; sit close to one another in the car; "claim" one another through your embrace when you're out in public!

- **Sexual Touching** - Soft skin touching is usually preferred over grabbing or mauling. Kiss "brushing" of neck, back, or hand is often appropriate. Try body massage with lotion or baby oil. Fabrics can accentuate touch so you might try silk sheets or silk nightwear.

Sharing Preferences Through Love Maps

I. Complete your "Love Map" — "From my point of view, a perfect sexually intimate time with my spouse would include the following:"

1.

2.

3.

4.

5.

6.

II. Marriage Intimacy
- Exchange your "Love Maps" - pick a private time and place.
- Discuss them as much as you are comfortable.
- Clarify and answer questions as appropriate.
- "Free" your spouse to fulfill as much of your Love Map as he or she is not comfortable with...don't "insist," get pushy or love conditionally!

III. Give to One Another — Scheduling two times of intimacy to fulfill both Love Maps
- Husband should first "Give" in fulfilling his wife's Love Map, with a subsequent time for the wife to "Give."
- Schedule (plan a time for this so you can both anticipate it).
- Throughout the day, spend moments anticipating the pleasures of the two of you "becoming one."
- Freely share all of yourself with one another.

Involving All Five Senses

Sexual closeness is oftentimes enhanced as more of the five senses are involved. Remembering that we see, touch, taste, hear and smell —get creative about involving more of your senses. To stimulate your creativity consider the following possibilities:

- **Sight**—soft lighting, intimate sleepwear, undressing one another
- **Touch**—body massage, bubble bath, different sleepwear fabrics, satin sheets
- **Taste**—soft kisses, fruit drinks, body lotions
- **Hear**—pleasant background music, sound tracks of surf or nature, soft whispers to one another
- **Smell**—scented candlelight, perfumed bath oils and powders, colognes and perfume

Take turns initiating and leading in your next two times of physical intimacy—each experimenting with involving all five senses. Use the "Love Map" exercise above to guide discussion.

Chapter Three

Dimensions
of Intimacy

Phil and Susy's Journey

When I arrived in Viet Nam I was assigned to a machine-gun team led by a battle-hardened soldier named Ralph. Ralph was the best machine-gunner in our outfit. We made an interesting team: one white, one black; one middle class, one well-to-do; one who had *inherited* social prestige, the other who *fought* for it. Staying alive required teamwork and unity. Many times, Ralph's keen knowledge of war led us out of a near-fatal position. But there came a time for me to reciprocate.

During a mission on November 7, 1967, Ralph and I were manning a position at the forward perimeter. The enemy attacked and soon a third of our company lay dead or wounded. Before we knew it, Ralph and I were caught in a crossfire. Over the roar of the automatic weapon fire, Ralph screamed, "Downer, I'm hit!" Instinctively, in the midst of enemy fire, I jumped up to help him. Actually, the bullet had only pierced his uniform but for a moment he thought the bullet had gone through him. He was OK and we both survived that night. In the midst of the battle he learned about me what I had already known about him - that I would risk my life for him.

The warrior in every man would like to be courageous, loyal and steadfast in battle. I exuded that kind of loyalty to a man I had only known for four months. However, to the only woman I've ever loved—my wife—I had forsaken courage and become a coward. I was totally selfish. My selective memory only recorded my wants, needs, and point of view, and steadfastly ignored Susy's. I risked my life for a fellow Marine but I would not lay it down for my lifetime partner, my wife. Even after becoming a Christian, I still often sought what was best for me and would plan and operate as though I were a Marine unit of one man. Quite often, men want to survive the war with valor and succeed in business with recognition, but too often we ignore the most important challenge - the spiritual war being waged against our family. We devote ourselves to everything other than God's priority for us - being faithful husbands and fathers.

Ralph and I were single-minded because we had a common goal of fighting well and surviving. The fear of death was our ever-present reminder that we must work together. In a strange way, war can unite two vastly different people. Ralph and I also shared our hopes and dreams of what we wanted to do when we returned to the "real world." Emotional bonding occurred as Ralph comforted me when John, a fellow Marine, fell on top of me riddled with bullets. And I, in turn, comforted Ralph when a booby trap blew off Willie's legs. Although we came from backgrounds where the races didn't mix, Ralph and I transcended superficial differences as we shared each other's food, provisions, ammo, and foxholes—without a second thought.

Living Vulnerably - A Prerequisite for Intimacy

Yes, I felt close to the men in my unit - a varied compilation of men who had agreed to a 13-month hitch with the fighting Fifth Marines in Vietnam. And yet I found it difficult to share spiritual, emotional and physical intimacy with this person with whom I had agreed to a "lifetime hitch." Emotional intimacy was difficult for me because in order to share my deep needs, passion and vision, I'd also have to share my fears, weaknesses and hurts. I had been taught to keep them to my self because "big boys don't cry." To me, physical intimacy just meant sex, which I pursued eagerly, but I ignored the caring touches, affectionate embraces, and tenderness associated with balanced physical intimacy. Men need to recognize that not only did some of God's greatest servants show tears and admit to weaknesses, but Jesus himself wept. He was truly acquainted with sorrow and grief, and when He hurt, He didn't just "stuff it." As followers of Christ, we too need to express our emotions and be vulnerable.

One of the greatest generals ever to walk the face of the earth, one who stood with great courage against impossible odds, was willing to admit weakness and failure. His name? Joshua.

> *"Then Joshua tore his clothes and fell facedown on the ground before the ark of the Lord, remaining there till evening. The elders of Israel did the same, and sprinkled dust on their heads. And Joshua said, 'Ah, sovereign Lord, why did you ever bring this people across the Jordan to deliver us into the hands of the Amorites to destroy us? O Lord, what can I say, now that Israel has been routed by its enemies'"* (Joshua 7:6-8).

Joshua's honest prayer, in which he confessed weakness, helplessness and humility, was heard by the Lord. God responded: "Rise up! The victory will be yours."

Following the example of Jesus and Joshua, we must be willing to share all of what's going on inside - our pain and our successes. In this chapter we'll explore these "dimensions" of intimacy and discuss practical "how-to's" of intimacy as God intended.

The Priority of Marriage Intimacy

Marriage intimacy powerfully impacts the effectiveness of a man's witness for Christ. Each day brings new reminders that only as a man's marriage and family are enjoying God's intended intimacy is there the "platform" for broader ministry to other people.

At CBMC, our vision is to saturate the business and professional community with the gospel of Jesus Christ by establishing, equipping, and mobilizing teams to operate in their neighborhoods and workplaces. Our strategy is first evangelism and then discipleship because it is through disciple-makers that God is changing the world. New converts, if left to themselves, have difficulty knowing how to mature in their Christian walk. They need one-on-one discipleship.

Carl, a friend of mine, who serves on the CBMC staff, had high hopes that his leadership team would become an effective combat unit in the battle for winning and discipling business and professional men and their wives and families in his large, metropolitan area.

However, after getting the leadership team together, Carl recognized that these men were not ready, willing or able to take on the vision of reaching their city for Jesus Christ, because, in different ways, the majority of the team had serious marital problems. Some were indifferent toward their wives, and others were too preoccupied with business and ministry to be the effective husband and father God called them to be. Before these men could conquer their city for Christ, they needed to focus on their marriages. To ignore the problems in their marriages would undoubtedly lead to failure as they attempted to be salt and light in their city. After spending over a year in a marriage study, Carl now has a team of men who are willing and able to impact their world.

Intimacy Developed in Small Groups

Susy and I are involved in a regular marriage intimacy home group. Our small group has become much deeper and closer than a typical Bible study with friends. We have shared the deep issues of life with one another, and now feel that we have a community of believers to which we could bring any problem and find their love, truth, empathy, wisdom, and godly support. These groups are also very effective tools for reaching unbelievers. In these groups you have the closeness everybody looked for (but didn't find) in the fraternity and sorority houses, and in the women's clubs and men's groups. These groups are based upon several premises:

- People must be honest, willing to share, and even willing to say when they're not willing to share.
- Everything shared must be held in confidence.
- The group should have a sustaining membership, without a lot of change, and meet regularly (at least once a month and probably twice or more a month is ideal).
- The focus should be on Christ and His work in our lives and marriages.
- His work should not just be studied but also applied.
- The group should be fun.

After focusing on marriage and family, these groups are a perfect place to begin a lifestyle evangelism study course called "Living Proof I" which will equip the group to find common ground and build relationships with unbelieving friends, and through those relationships allow God to reach them for Christ.

David and Teresa's Reflections

What Phil has shared is absolutely true. If a man or woman wants to be effective in ministry, the first priority must be his or her marriage and family. Let's further explore the dimensions of marital intimacy.

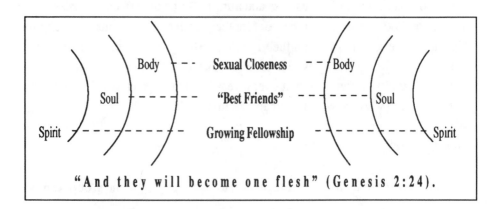

Body --- Sexual Closeness --- Body

Soul --- "Best Friends" --- Soul

Spirit --- Growing Fellowship --- Spirit

"And they will become one flesh" (Genesis 2:24).

Dimensions of Marital Intimacy

For relationships to be knit closely together in marriage or in families, sharing must be encouraged. "Closeness" doesn't just automatically happen because we have the same last name or live under the same roof! "Becoming one" in marriage involves the freedom to share all of oneself - spirit, soul, and body.

The chart on the previous page illustrates how a husband and wife can develop marital intimacy in three dimensions. Marriages need nourishment and attention in each of these three areas. Just as we need air, food, and water to be healthy physically, our marriages have essential nourishment needs. A growing, healthy, and balanced marital relationship is one where each partner is enjoying the abundance of intimacy - spirit, soul, and body.

Often, couples may enjoy a certain level of spiritual compatibility, have a tolerable friendship, but have a problematic sex life. Other couples might enjoy a growing friendship and a satisfying sex life, but have no real spiritual closeness. Marital happiness is achieved when all three dimensions are constantly being nourished and experienced.

Spiritual Oneness - Saints Enjoying Fellowship

To achieve spiritual oneness, each partner must have a personal, vital, and growing relationship with Christ, and then learn to relate to their spouse on a spiritual basis. A good place to begin is to pray together. If either partner is uncomfortable praying aloud, simply hold hands and pray silently.

Another way to develop spiritual oneness is to begin a joint prayer list and share together in the blessing of intercession and answered prayer. Other ways to develop spiritual intimacy include: discussing selected Scriptures together, ministering to others, and attending or teaching a Bible study together.

Soulish Oneness - Best Friends

The soul realm involves the mind, will, and emotions. Closeness is developed as thoughts are shared and time is given in the loving act of attentive listening; emotions are identified and openly shared in a receptive and understanding environment; and a closeness of will is realized as common interests are shared, mutual goals are identified and achieved and oneness in decision-making is practiced.

Sexual Oneness - Lovers

Physical closeness requires open communication, a priority time commitment, and the freshness of creativity. Plan a weekend away without the children. Plan two sexual times together, just to focus on "giving" to your spouse, not taking.

Marital Intimacy Inventory

After you've taken a few minutes to reflect on your relationship with your spouse, indicate your perception of your degree of intimacy in the three areas of spirit, soul, and body. Place an X on the scale below to signify your view of the relationship.

1. The **spiritual** dimension of our relationship is:

    lacking in intimacy 1————————5————————10 *very intimate*

    What aspect of your spiritual relationship would you most like to see changed or improved in your marriage?

    _____

2. The **emotional** or friendship dimension of our relationship is:

    lacking in intimacy 1————————5————————10 *very intimate*

    What aspect of your emotional relationship would you most like to see changed or improved in your marriage?

    _____

3. The **physical** dimension of our relationship is:

    lacking in intimacy 1————————5————————10 *very intimate*

What aspect of your physical relationship would you most like to see changed or improved in your marriage?

_____

_____

Encouraging Vulnerable Communication

"...perfect love casts out all fear" (1 John 4:18-19). The "perfect" love of this passage is God's love...sacrificial, giving and filled with initiative. As believers, we have received His divine love.

Much of what hinders vulnerability is rooted in FEAR...fear of being reject-ed or misunderstood, fear of inadequacy or retaliation. As we share His agape love with spouse, children and others, it ministers freedom from fear. A very practical experience of this freedom comes as we engage in intimate communi-cation.

Since God's perfect love is sacrificially given and takes initiative, one way to encourage deepened communication is by ministering reassurances such as:

- I want to reassure you of my commitment to listen to your heart, your feelings, and your needs—in order to better know you and love you.
- I will make our sharing times a "safe place" for you to express your most intimate feelings. I commit not to withdraw, reject or criticize.
- I'm committed to keep our intimate sharing times confidential ...just between you and me, and to never use what you share against you in any way.
- I see the importance of us sometimes needing to agree to dis-agree.
- You don't need to "be me." I want you to have the freedom to "be you" and all God desires for you to be.
- As I identify barriers within me during our sharing, I'm com-mitted to address them, resolve them and remove them so they'll no longer be a hindrance to our sharing.
- Realizing my need to be responsible for my emotions and

behavior, I will not blame you or rationalize my behavior.

- When I let you down in some way and hurt you, I'm committed to bring healing and resolution as God sorrows my heart and I seek forgiveness.
- I want to reassure you of my commitment to better love you unconditionally. This is best demonstrated when, even though I may be disappointed or hurt in someway, I still lovingly give to you anyway.
- I'm committed to you and our relationship, and want to more consistently verbalize and demonstrate my care and love for you.

We will not sense the oneness in our marriage that God intends until we develop intimacy in all three dimensions: spirit, soul, and body. One out of three or even two out of three is insufficient. The following exercises will help us further explore what it means to become friends, lovers and saints.

Take a minute to reflect back on these 10 specific statements of "reassurance" and identify one or two you want to verbalize to your spouse this week.

Loving Your Spouse - Spirit, Soul, and Body... Becoming Saints, Friends, and Lovers

The three dimensions of intimacy relate to the three different "parts" of a human being: *"May God himself, the God of peace, sanctify you through and through. May your whole spirit, soul, and body be kept blameless at the coming of our Lord Jesus Christ"* (I Thessalonians 5:23). It shouldn't surprise us that the Triune God who manifests Himself as Father, Son and Holy Spirit would likewise create us similarly "complex!" The complexity is compounded as two become one in the marriage relationship. Three uniquely different Greek words for love reinforce these dimensions of intimacy.

Saints Sharing Fellowship

- **Agape** – is used in the New Testament to describe the attitude of God toward His Son (John 17:26), toward humanity (John 3:16) and toward those who believe upon His Son (John 14:21). "Agape" is then used to convey God's desire that believers share this love with others — including spouses and children (John 13:34). "Agape" is shown through its action, initiative, commitment and giving — not through its "feeling." "Agape" is an expression of God's Spirit and it is impossible to "produce" through self-will.

> *"Agape" is shown through its action, initiative, commitment and giving.*

When two saints share fellowship, we see two recipients of transforming grace living in the awe and wonder of being loved by their Creator (John 1:16); two mere humans experiencing together the inexpressible joy of living today as children of God, partakers of the divine nature (2 Peter 1:4); two aliens and strangers walking in this world, but not of this world (1 Peter 2:11, John 17:16), laboring together as ambassadors for Christ; being transformed together into HIS image (2 Corinthians 3:18, 5:20); longing together for His soon return (1 John 3:2).

Study Questions

Pause and reflect about how God has abundantly expressed his agape love toward you: God has...

_____

_____

How could this type of love be better expressed in your marriage? I could...

_____

_____

Friends Sharing Friendship

- **Phileo** – is distinguished from agape in that it speaks of tender affection and represents the emotional aspect of a relationship. Phileo speaks of two hearts knit together in tenderness of mutual companionship. A descriptive characterization would be to affectionately CHERISH a special person.

> *"Phileo" speaks of tender affection and represents the emotional aspect of a relationship.*

Two hearts stirred with a cherishing of one another—this dimension provides the emotional content. Sometimes "up" and sometimes "down," these feelings remind us that this relationship is active! Alive! And changing! Common interests and goals are identified and deepened as mutual support is given; communication grows through open expression and vulnerability. Thoughts linger over the specialness of one another; two people have become to one another "best friends."

Recalling that Abraham was referred to as a "friend of God," write about how your friendship with the Lord might be deepened. (see John 15:13-15)

_____

_____

What practical steps could you take toward becoming "best friends" with your spouse?

_____

_____

Lovers Sharing Passion

■ Eros – is the word from which EROTIC comes; it speaks of sensual fulfillment and the physical pleasures of sexual expression. A God given "boundary" to confine these pleasures to the marriage relationship is given often in the Scriptures.

Physical excitement, expectation and arousal prompt a desire for marriage partners to "become one flesh" (Genesis 2:24). Physical attraction is involved and anticipation of physical "togetherness" grows into passion; thoughts of physical oneness stir a desire to touch and to verbalize; a mutuality of sensitive "giving" to the passionate needs of another unites two friends as lovers.

Reminded that it was God who created sexual intimacy for marriage, how might a couples' spiritual oneness and friendship be related to sexual satisfaction?

"Eros" is the word from which EROTIC comes.

_____

_____

What additional sensitivity, care, initiative and giving might you express toward your spouse to deepen sexual intimacy?

_____

_____

Marriage "Staff Meetings"

"Do two walk together unless they have agreed to do so?" (Amos 3:3).

Developing and maintaining marriage and family intimacy requires that a husband and wife spend quality, consistent time together. The external stresses of work, carpools, child raising, and checkbooks need not take their toll on marital "oneness" if couples will take the time to "manage" family events before they "manage" you! Even Jesus, during His public ministry, found it necessary to consistently withdraw from the crowds and spend time with His disciples for special times of sharing and encouragement.

It's inconceivable that a successful business could operate without regular staff meetings. Why then do most families try to operate without a regular time of planned communication? If it works in business, it will work for the family.

Here are some *characteristics* of a successful Marriage Staff Meeting.

1. **Schedule a time** - don't leave it to chance! Preferably, the staff meeting will be a "standing appointment," occurring the same time, same place each week. Perhaps a good time would be over lunch on Thursday, or Tuesday night after the children are asleep, or during Saturday morning breakfast. Some couples' schedules are such that the time has to change each week. If so, prioritize scheduling the staff meeting for the coming week.

2. **Prioritize the time** - as much as possible, make it "inviolate." Once the time is scheduled - protect it! Treat the appointment like it's the most important item on your schedule - because it is. Prioritizing the Marriage Staff Meeting will produce a renewed sense of closeness (one wife cried with joy when her husband remembered their staff meeting and turned down a golf date).

3. **Protect the time** - prevent interruptions and distractions. Find a "quiet" place at home, or if necessary, meet away from the home and office. Avoid phone-calls or visitors if possible.

A fearful thought for many couples may be "What in the world will we talk about?" A productive staff meeting might have this *agend*a:

1. **Consider calendar coordination** - look ahead to the coming week. What's planned? What's the children's schedule for the week? Who's working late? What social activities are scheduled? Operate from a principle of agreeing on time commitments which affect the entire family before making these commitments. Plan your next couple "date" and your next family outing. You'll even find that there's often great value in calendaring some of your lovemaking times!

2. **Listen to one another** - one spouse or the other may just need to talk. When listening, establish eye contact and give undivided attention. Be quick to offer comfort, encouragement, and support. Avoid advice-giving, arguing, belittling, teaching, or lecturing. Be open to share hopes and dreams, feelings and insights about recent moodiness, and concerns and fears about the marriage, kids, money, and the future. The power of giving undivided attention allows you to enter into another person's "world" and really get to know them.

3. **Discuss family goals** - monitor their progress. As marriage communication deepens, written annual goals need to be developed for the family and broken down into quarterly/monthly target dates. Goals and plans could be developed in these areas: marriage, social, financial, personal, family, educational, spiritual, and professional.
   - Does the budget look "tight" this coming week? If so, how can we all help?
   - What's our next planned major household expenditure and how could we all better "contribute" to bring it about?
   - Have we scheduled our family vacation? Reservations made? Itinerary set?

- Have we decided on some new couple friends we want to get to know this year?
- How are our personal goals progressing...reading, diet, exercise, hobby...and how can we encourage and support one another?
- What aspects of church life do we want to be involved in this next quarter?
- What's the next fun marriage "get-away" we have planned?
- What projects can we plan which focus on sharing Christ with our neighbors?

4. **Discuss parenting plans** - if you don't become united on parenting issues, the kids will "divide and conquer"!
   - Discuss significant discipline issues; what seems to be working and what doesn't.
   - Plan family times together plus "quality times" for each parent with each child.
   - Discuss and agree upon parenting responsibilities and schedules for the next week. Who's needing help? Who's needing a "break" from the kids?
   - What goals seem reasonable for our children this quarter in the areas of behavior, attitude, and responsibilities, and how can we work together to achieve them?

5. **Engage in productive "feedback"** - lovingly share areas of irritation, hurt, and disappointment. In an intimate relationship, there will be the freedom to, *"Speak the truth in love"* (Ephesians 4:15). A marriage staff meeting provides a "neutral" setting in which touchy issues can be honestly shared in an atmosphere of acceptance and teachableness. For instance, you might need to share:
   - "I sure miss being alone with you, could we plan a 'date' together?"
   - "It would mean a lot to me if we could remain in agreement in front of the kids...and discuss any differences privately."
   - "Sometimes it seems your initial response to situations is negative. Could we talk about why that is and discuss how I could be helpful in encouraging optimism?"
   - "Last Tuesday I felt embarrassed when... could we talk about it?"

6. **Share words of appreciation** - for "who" your spouse is and "what" he or she has done. Use your weekly "staff meeting" as a reminder that your spouse is a blessing to you! They do have good qualities! For instance, you might share:

   - "Thanks for your help this week with the kids."
   - "I was reminded this week of how much I appreciate your diligence in seeing that things get done around the house."
   - "You are a very giving person, and it really showed this week when you..."
   - "I love you, just for who you are."

Establishing and maintaining a meaningful, weekly Marriage Staff Meeting will be one of the most important steps you make in pursuing wholesome and intimate marriage and family relationships. Conflicts, hurts, and misunderstandings will be resolved, and a oneness will develop, allowing you to experience the joy of "walking together" according to Amos 3:3

Intimacy Exercises

Sharing Your Wishes

During your next Marriage Staff Meeting, try this exercise. It will help you identify and share areas in which you think the relationship could be improved through vulnerable sharing.

1. List up to six "Wishes" relative to your relationship. - Be specific and positive. Examples: I'm hoping you can become more comfortable initiating affection with me. I would enjoy regularly scheduled "dates" together at least twice a month.

    "Wish List"

    _____

    _____

    _____

    _____

    _____

    _____

2. Share your lists with your spouse - Sharing "wishes" helps avoid the destructive cycle of:
    ■ Having expectations and anticipations (i.e., wishes) of another person.
    ■ Not communicating these wishes.
    ■ Becoming hurt or angry when these expectations aren't met! This isn't fair to either person.

3. Exchange lists. It will help you remember your partner's wishes. Begin working on areas that your spouse wants changed.

Learning to Identify People's Needs by Listening to What They Say

We all have important intimacy needs. These needs are "built into the DNA of the human race," and they serve as catalyst for our motivation and they strongly affect our behavior. Many people are unaware of these needs in their lives and therefore don't know how to correctly express their needs when they are neglected. Even if we acknowledge our "neediness," we often forget to properly express our needs to our loved ones.

Listed below are some phrases you might hear from your spouse, children, or friends. Beside each phrase, write down the need that's being expressed by each statement. Possible needs are: acceptance, approval, security, respect, encouragement, attention, support, comfort, affection, and appreciation.

- "You're too busy."
- "Look what I did."
- "Do you mind asking my opinion?"
- "Will you always love me?"
- "I just can't do this."
- "I feel out of place."
- "I've had a bad day."
- "I feel like a failure."
- "Could we spend more time together?"
- "I'm really upset!"
- "Hold me."
- "Would you help me?"
- "I have a big nose."
- "What do you think of what I've done?"
- "I can't do anything right!"
- "I've had it!"
- "You're always making all the decisions."
- "I just want a place we can call home."

Try using this exercise to prompt discussion of individual intimacy needs during a Marriage Staff Meeting or during a family night. This exercise is from the Intimate Life booklet entitled *Top Ten Intimacy Needs*. To order, see the information page at the end of this book.

Chapter Four

High Performance, Damaged Emotions

Phil and Susy's Journey

I remember the day my father, Sam Downer, and I met Jim Ling, the "L" behind the giant LTV conglomerate, on an elevator. It happened to be the day that LTV filed for Chapter 11 bankruptcy protection. My father, a senior vice president with LTV Aerospace, said, "Good morning, Jim, how is it going?" With an air of confidence, control and outward calmness that defied the newspaper clippings I had read that morning, he said in a firm tone, "Fine, Sam, fine, all things considered." I thought to myself, "Wow, what a man, what a rock, what a tower of strength. That's the way I want to be." Here was the ideal man: Perform but don't feel.

But my concept of the "ideal man" started developing many years before that elevator ride. While growing up, I remember an "Ozzie and Harriet" home by day but fighting, crashing sounds and angry voices at night. Our home was filled with strife and turmoil but everyone pretended that everything was fine. I unknowingly embraced the misconception that pain and problems were to be stuffed. Again the subtle but ever-present message was "perform but don't feel."

It wasn't until I buried my dad that I first learned that although he had been a very successful businessman, he had been fired from three different jobs during his career as he made his way to the top of the corporate ladder. I know dad must have experienced much pain through those years, but he never told anyone. Words like "failure, can't, hurt, and need" were simply not a part of our family's vocabulary. The hallmarks of our house were pride, accomplishment, strength, coolness, and confronting the next challenge. Even while watching a touching scene on *Wagon Train, Gunsmoke* or *Bonanza,* dad and I would respond with humor or sarcasm, always hiding our emotions.

"Big boys don't cry," and "Marines don't retreat." That was my training, that was my conviction, and that was a lie! After becoming a Christian many things changed, but the firewall around my emotions only received a few chinks. Occasionally I would express emotion privately with God in prayer, but those times were few and far between.

My lack of emotionality rendered me incompetent to relate to others on an emotional level. Several years after becoming a Christian, I was the leader of a weekend retreat where several men were to share their life experiences. As one man was "rehearsing" the talk he was to make at the retreat, he shared how one of his four daughters had died from a dreaded disease. He vulnerably described the heartbreak, pain and helplessness he felt about the situation. When he finished, I was the first one to speak. Instead of sharing words of comfort, I piped up with my analytical mind, and said, "Well, Keith, that was good, but I really think you could sharpen your focus by using a few more verses, and there were a couple of other points that you left out of the suggested outline..." and for about ten minutes I droned on with my heartless, emotionless analysis. I totally missed the message. I was so consumed with the details and mechanics of his speech, I completely missed hearing his hurting heart. My response just added to my friend's pain and sorrow.

On another occasion, one of my fellow attorneys came to me after being humiliated in the courtroom. He too was hurting, but true to form, I started to rattle through my analysis of what he did wrong, and how he could improve on his courtroom technique. My friend didn't hear a word I had said; I'm sure that he felt like I was only interested in his performance, not his pain. Since that incident, he never confided in me again, except to share his victories, and only from a distance.

As Christians, we often act as though we are robots, incapable of feelings. Then we try to reach out to a broken-hearted generation and we wonder why we are so ineffective in our ministry. It's true that the gospel contains the facts about Christ's life, sacrificial death, and resurrection. But it's possible to keep that information in the mind and never have it take the 13 inch plunge to the heart. There must be an experiential and emotional aspect of relating to Christ as Lord and Savior. But sadly, we Christians often approach the lost world with a facade of perfection, an arrogance of presuming to have all the answers, and an unwillingness to get close, be vulnerable, and to hurt, bleed and feel with men and women.

Another example of this is when my spiritual father, Jim, took me on a follow-up visit to see a man who had shown interest in the gospel after attending a CBMC meeting. Jim was thrilled as he watched me share my testimony and then take Aaron through the "Steps to Peace with God" booklet which explains the gospel. I then proceeded to ask Aaron if he would be willing to pray to receive Christ, and after we talked for a few more moments, I led him through the sinner's prayer and Aaron prayed to receive Christ! After the prayer, I

...my "emotional cup" was so full I found myself constantly escaping into performance and activity, seeking to control most everything and everyone around me.

glanced up and noticed Jim quietly wiping away a tear from the corner of each eye. As we walked back to my office, Jim was leaping for joy and praising the Lord but I analyzed the situation in a rather ho-hum attitude of, "Well, we did what we were supposed to do, and it worked."

As Jim and I continued to meet, the Lord began to show me that I was only focused on objectives, goals, truth, and methods for taking truth to people who needed it. But I really lacked compassion, empathy, and a gentle, listening spirit - essential qualities for impacting a hurting world. I realized that my emotions had been damaged, beaten down and suppressed for most of my life. As we'll explore in this chapter, my "emotional cup" was so full I found myself constantly escaping into performance and activity, seeking to control most everything and everyone around me. And when control was lost, anger came forth, wounding the ones I loved and sought to minister to.

On the second night of our honeymoon I saw a side of Phil that I didn't know existed. He lashed out at me with uncontrollable anger. Frankly, neither one of us can remember what the issue was, but it was something insignificant over which I had no control. I cried myself to sleep that night for the first time in my life. Hurt, anger and fear began to accumulate in my "emotional cup" and eventually my love for Phil grew cold.

From that point on, divorce was always in the back of my mind. However, I chose to stick it out for several reasons, none of which are very laudable. One reason we didn't divorce is that I hated to admit that I had made a mistake in marrying Phil. My self-centered pride in the fact that "no one in our family has ever been divorced" actually provided protection for us until Christ could make real changes. Also, I loved law school and law practice and they provided a strong diversion from our marital strife. Thirdly, not to my credit but to Phil's, he was always sorry for the trouble he brought to our marriage and really tried to change, although without Christ that was impossible. His sincere apologies would endear himself to me and I would think, "maybe this time he has really changed." I also didn't want to divorce Phil because deep inside I knew he loved me and my rejection of him would have been devastating. There was one other reason—I would not have been welcomed home without Phil.

Throughout my growing up years, my mother and father modeled commitment, even though they came to Christ about the same time Phil and I did. They were raised by godly parents, whose principles and practices permeated their lives. Although I didn't know the Bible verse, I knew that I was supposed to leave them and become one with Phil. My pride prevented me from sharing with mom what I was going through and I was also reluctant because my parents had taught me that divorce was not an option.

David and Teresa's Reflections

Phil and Susy experienced a lot of hurt, Phil from his family of origin and both of them in their marriage. And hurt which is not properly dealt with accumulates! Let's explore how this happens, the symptoms we might exhibit when we get emotionally "full" and the joy which comes from being healed.

Healing Unhealed Emotional Pain

To hurt is to be human! No one likes to hurt, but the issue is not "if" we'll be hurt, just "when?," "how much?" and "by whom?" Trying to eliminate or minimize our vulnerability to pain simply makes us impersonal and "cold." The more invulnerable we become, the more impersonal and "machine-like" we become. Machines don't hurt but people do and God created us that way. God created us with emotional and relational needs and with them comes the inevitability of pain as they may go unmet.

The issue then is what have I done with the pain? Have I resolved the pain or minimized and denied it? The same is true of marriage: healthy marriages heal and resolve inevitable pain rather than ignore the pain or retaliate. In the same way, the functional family heals inevitable hurt and provides an open/approachable environment in which this takes place. The dysfunctional family refuses to deal with family pain and instead of an open and approachable family environment, common family rules would be "don't feel," "don't trust," and "don't talk"—particularly about problems or pain.

Common Objections to Dealing with Pain

"It was all so long ago."
"You can't undo the past."
"Time heals all...doesn't it?"

Many find themselves seemingly trapped between an unchangeable past and fear of change in the present. The issue is not how long ago the pain occurred but rather is the pain still "alive" within you? Time is a necessary ingredient for healing but not a sufficient one…more is needed! For years and years, has the sun gone down on anger (Ephesians 4:26)? Has the fear which was not from God been removed (2 Timothy 1:7; 1 John 4:18-19)? Have you found freedom from inner shame (condemnation) and has the God of all comfort been allowed to comfort your hurt (Romans 8:1, 2 Corinthians 1:4)? Surely part of God's abundance for us is to remove the "sting" from the memories…the sting of anger, fear, shame or hurt (John 10:10).

Before continuing, review the "emotional cup" exhibit and reflect on the following questions:

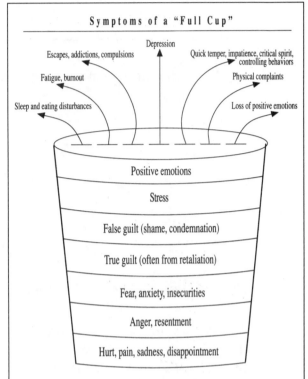

1. What overflow symptoms (temper, escaping, loss of positive emotions, etc) do you exhibit? What symptoms does your spouse exhibit?

_____

_____

2. What unresolved hurts might be unresolved in you? In your spouse?

_____

_____

3. What anger might still be present in you? In your spouse?

_____

_____

4. What guilt do I sense over ways in which I've hurt my
    spouse?

_____

_____

Better Understanding Emotional Pain

Hurt and Anger—Two Sides of The Same Pain

Consider the pain which comes from rejection, ridicule, and marriage infidelity. First there is a deep sense of hurt and loss (sadness, vulnerable feelings
of a trust betrayed). Next we normally have feelings of anger, which often
"cover" the feelings of hurt. The hurt feelings leave us violated and saddened
and we suffer a diminished sense of "self" and are vulnerable to more pain, so
exposed that anger rises up to protect us. For many, the angry feelings are so automatic that there is no connection made between hurt and anger. Feelings of loss, and
the vulnerability surrounding them, are tender feelings — but few can tolerate such
vulnerable pain so anger toward another rises up to distract and defend us. Thus, I
hide my vulnerability and loss by being angry at you!

Hurts Involve a "Loss" to be Mourned

Human hurt is often defined as a violation of trust that results in a loss of
something deeply personal. Related to human intimacy needs, hurt is associated
with the loss of these needs being met—rejection rather than acceptance;
neglect rather than attention; abuse rather than security. The pain of personal
loss must be felt, shared, expressed, validated, and then comforted. Even
unhealed hurts from the past must still be mourned.

Anger Wears Many Masks

The anger of unhealed hurts may be exhibited in a variety of ways. Among them are: impatience, quick-temper, depression, addictions, mistrust or suspicion, self-pity, and jealously, plus certain passive-aggressive behaviors like procrastinating, avoiding, silence, sarcasm. The process of healing must involve "working through" and releasing the anger.

Healing Marital Hurts Which Hinder Oneness

Hurts don't simply "go away." Time doesn't spontaneously heal resentment and trying harder doesn't compensate for guilt. The Bible, however, does not leave us without instruction. Prayerfully consider the following admonitions as you prepare for followup "homework" with your spouse: **Unresolved Anger**— Anger, bitterness and resentment require forgiveness—*"Let all bitterness and wrath and clamor and slander be put away from you...forgiving each other..."* (Ephesians 4:31-32). **Unconfessed Guilt**—Unconfessed guilt from either active or passive retaliation requires confession. *"If we confess our sins, He is faithful and righteous to forgive us..."* (1 John 1:9). *"Confess your faults to one another and pray for one another that you may be healed"* (James 5:16). The Experiencing Biblical Truth exercise involves a marital project for healing unresolved hurts. The project places a high priority on the following principles:

Personal Responsibility

I must give an account of myself, not others...to God (Romans 14:12)...otherwise I live in a world of rationalizing, justifying and blaming: "I wouldn't do that if you wouldn't..."

Accountability to God

Hurting my spouse also "hurts" God...and needs His forgiveness. It's sobering to realize that my selfishness, or my unloving attitude or my abusive and demeaning words were exactly why Christ had to die for me!

Confession of My Faults as Wrong

Quit "confessing" your spouse's faults and confess your own! I was "wrong" is much better than saying I am "sorry," since "wrong" tends to convey more responsibility, remorse and repentance. The word "confess" means to "agree with," and God says these things are wrong.

Requesting Forgiveness — "Will You Forgive Me?"

The vulnerability of this confession conveys important humility as well as challenges a spouse with the responsibility to forgive.

"Forgiveness is a Choice — Not a Feeling!"

The Biblical admonition to "put away" anger, wrath, and bitterness...forgiving one another is a command to choose to forgive (release; turn loose of). Seal this choice by verbalizing your forgiveness, "I forgive you." Forgiveness is also an issue of stewardship; first we receive God's forgiveness and then we are challenged to share it with others.

Prayer Together Encourages Oneness

After confession and forgiveness, begin experiencing the intimacy of prayer together by holding hands and praying silently together.

New Memories Begin Replacing Old Ones

Old memories of hurt are now being "renewed" with new memories of your spouse confessing wrong and requesting forgiveness; new memories of you verbalizing "I forgive you"; new memories of sealing this healing time with prayer. *"Be transformed by the renewing of your mind"* (Romans 12:2).

Staff Meeting and Family Night Ideas

Schedule a time when you and your spouse can identify hurts and receive God's forgiveness. Refer to the "Healing Family Emotional Hurts" material (see Experiencing Biblical Truth exercise) and then schedule a time to finish the exercise on confession and forgiveness.

Discuss the need for a family time of healing hurts (particularly with school age children and adolescents). If significant hurts exist between children and parents they don't simply "go away!" Schedule a family night to introduce the Healing Hurts exercise; give each member a week to work through identifying hurts and gaining God's forgiveness, and then schedule confession and forgiveness for the next family night with parents making their apologies first (father leads).

Godly Sorrow
Produces
Repentance

In a day when true, life change seems elusive, and any Christ-like distinction seems lost in secular culture, the fact that Godly sorrow produces repentance is hopeful, good news. In the midst of continuing to *"do the very things I don't want to do"* (Romans 7), this promise regarding repentance is indeed refreshing. The focus of Paul's burden for the Corinthians is not the outcome of repentance but rather the godly sorrow that actually produces (prompts, brings forth) genuine repentance. Before there's the external evidence of a changed life, there's the internal work of godly sorrow. A deep, emotional work of the heart must precede a change of behavior, attitude, and action. In his first letter, Paul challenged the Corinthians to a brokenness of heart and in this second letter he rejoices with them in the blessed outcome. It's a surprising and emotional journey. It's also a very intimate journey as the Father reveals His pain to His children.

The Reality of Godly Sorrow

In contrast to the sorrow of this world, godly sorrow is timeless and eternal. In this world we experience tribulation and trials; struggles and losses take their toll. We constantly deal with the reality of rejections, regrets, disappointments, and pain, but we're not left alone in this journey because we have a Great High Priest who has gone before us (Hebrews 4:15), and who was acquainted with grief (Isaiah 53:3). Through the provision of divine comfort we experience blessing in our mourning (Matthew 5:4) as it comes through Him and others (2 Corinthians 1:2-4). Still this sorrow, as deep and penetrating as it is, remains of this world, common to this world and this life.

So what can we say about this godly sorrow that is not of this world? It's His sorrow and therefore called "godly." His sorrow can be revealed, shared, and imparted to the attentive hearts of His children.

> *It's a certain promise, a bold declaration - godly sorrow produces repentance!*

Imagine that one of your dearest friends is about to share with you some of the things that have broken his heart, causing him deep sorrow. Encourage him to share with you his pain?

_____

_____

_____

The Reason for Godly Sorrow

Godly sorrow speaks of *His* pain. The pain of a Father rejected in eternity past by His created hosts (Isaiah 14: 12-14), betrayed in the garden by the "very good" of His creation (Genesis 3), and repeatedly forsaken by His people (Exodus 32:7-10). Surely there is a sorrow-filled heart behind these words: *"Then the Lord saw that the wickedness of man was great on the earth and that every intent of the thoughts of his heart was only evil continually...and the Lord was sorry that He had made man on the earth and He was grieved in His heart"* (Genesis 6:5-6).

To experience godly sorrow is to share in the Father's pain; the pain of a loving Father who for us would:

- watch Him who knew no sin...become sin (2 Corinthians 5:21),
- allow the perfect One...to be wounded, bruised and chastised (Isaiah 53:4-5),
- hear His only begotten Son utter these words...*"My God, My God, why have You forsaken Me?"* (Matthew 27:46).

As we consider God's sorrow, our hearts should soften in sadness and grow quiet in brokenness as we consider our contribution to His pain. Worldly sorrow focuses on our grief, what "we" did. Likewise, condemnation produces a type of sorrow, but it's a sorrow focused on "how terrible I am." But, Godly sorrow shatters that self-focus as our heart ponders what we've done to the Father and His Son.

As we consider God's sorrow, our hearts should soften in sadness and grow quiet in brokenness as we consider our contribution to His pain.

Write about your heartfelt emotions concerning the Father's pain and rejection...particularly as you recall the Father hearing His only Son cry *"My God, My God, why have You forsaken Me?"* What do you feel for the Father?

_____

_____

_____

_____

The Receiving of Godly Sorrow

The Father vulnerably reveals His heart, His pain - but not to the flippant or to those who are busy or preoccupied. He only trusts His sorrow-filled heart to those who can be still enough to know Him, patient enough to wait. "Sorrow" is not a "heady" thing to be dissected, discussed, and debated as doctrine. It's a personal thing between a Father and a loved one, a tender issue of the heart, an emotional issue of the soul.

> *...it's a personal thing between a Father and a loved one, a tender issue of the heart, an emotional issue of the soul.*

It comes by way of the Spirit's conviction and my confession. Only the Spirit can convict (John 16:8), and only I can confess (1 John 1:9, James 5:16). The Holy Spirit will fulfill His role, convicting me of selfishness, a critical spirit, pride, and disrespect - specific offenses toward God and others. And then comes my part, genuine confession - "saying the same" about my selfishness, criticism, pride, and disrespect as the Father says. More than mere intellectual agreement of wrong or a volitional voicing of regret, "to confess" is an emotional issue of godly sorrow. In the stillness of time and the quietness of things divine, my heart cries out in agreement with the Father's sorrow:

- Your Son was wounded for my transgressions...my selfishness and pride
- Your Son was bruised for my iniquities...my critical spirit and disrespect. *"Against You and You only, have I sinned"* (Psalm 51:4).

- It was because of my sin that you had to hear those soul-piercing words, "My God, My God, why have You forsaken Me?"

Heartfelt confession will produce godly sorrow. No longer will there be self-defense, pretense, and posturing—only a broken and contrite heart. Entering into the intimacy of His suffering eliminates the "heady" pursuits to "understand" and to be "understood."

Study Question

Write from your heart concerning your response to the Father's pain:

_____

_____

The Results of Godly Sorrow

The results from such an encounter spring forth like scent-filled blossoms on a well nurtured plant. The results, both internal and external, are not manufactured, forced, or produced by a "grit-your-teeth and bear it" type of obedience. They come humbly, gently, and supernaturally. The *"love of Christ that constrains us"* (2 Corinthians 5:14) is the power that will change us.

The first result is grateful rejoicing, as confession frees us of guilt. Godly sorrow produces a joy in being forgiven and grateful thanksgiving ushers me into worship.

As to my guilt - *"The Lord was pleased to crush Him...He would render Him as a guilt offering"* (Isaiah 53:10).

As to my sorrow - *"Deliver me from guilt, O God...then my tongue will joyfully sing of Thy righteousness"* (Psalm 51:14).

As to my grateful thanksgiving - *"O Lord open my eyes that my mouth may declare Thy praise...for the sacrifices of God are a broken spirit, a broken and contrite heart"* (Psalm 51:15-17).

Godly sorrow also produces repentance - changes that make me more and more like Christ. It's a lasting impression on my life that I've been with Him; having entered into the fellowship of His sufferings, having shared intimately with Him in His sorrow, I can never be the same again.

> The *"love of Christ that constrains us"* (2 Corinthians 5:14) is the power that will change us.

Study Questions

Write about your gratefulness:

_____

_____

_____

Write about your anticipated areas of repentance and change:

_____

_____

_____

"Deliver me from guilt, O God...then my tongue will joyfully sing of Thy righteousness" (Psalm 51:14).

    Special Note: For some, this may be the first time you have personally associated your sin with Christ's death. By faith, if you will receive His forgiveness, He will cleanse you. Ask your spouse, pastor, group leader, or Christian friend to share with you how you can know Christ and the full pardon of sin.

Healing
Family
Emotional Hurts

> *"Put away all bitterness and anger — and be kind, tender-hearted, forgiving each other"* *(Ephesians 4:31-32).*

Here are six progressive steps which will lead to emotional healing.

1. Identify Hurt

Alone, list ways in which I have hurt my spouse and my children. For instance, "I've been: selfish, critical, negative, insensitive, disrespectful, verbally abusive, unsupportive, ungrateful, unfaithful, rejecting, unforgiving." Specific hurtful events, fights, arguments or "scenes" may also need to be confessed - use extra paper as needed!

_____

_____

_____

_____

2. Gain God's Forgiveness

Confess to God and receive His forgiveness. 1 John 1:9 says, *"If we confess our sins He (God) is faithful and just to forgive us and to cleanse us from all unrighteousness."* Example: "God, I have deeply hurt you and my spouse (or child) by being selfish, critical, negative, insensitive, disrespectful, verbally abusive, unsupportive, ungrateful, unfaithful, rejecting, unforgiving. These are very wrong and I ask you to forgive me. Thank you for doing so and I ask you to change me into the kind of person I need to be."

3. Confess Wrongs and Choose to Forgive

Together, share your lists and request forgiveness. James 5:16 says, *"Confess your faults to one another and pray for one another that you may be healed."* (We encourage husbands and fathers to confess first.) Example: "I've seen that I've hurt you deeply by being selfish, critical, negative, insensitive, disrespectful, verbally abusive, unsupportive, ungrateful, unfaithful, rejecting, unforgiving. I have been very wrong. Will you forgive me?" ("Wrong" is better than "sorry" since confess means "to agree with" God and God has said these things are wrong.)

4. Respond: "I forgive you"

Remember: Forgiveness is a choice, not primarily a feeling! The question is not, "do you feel like forgiving, "but rather," will you?" Will you release (drop) the hurt? Only then will anger dissipate and new feelings come! Also remember that you have first been forgiven by God...you now have the privilege of sharing some of His forgiveness with others.

Other areas to confess: It might be important to ask, "Are there other major hurts that I've not seen that need my apology? Please share them with me so I can confess them now and seek your forgiveness."

Next: Wife shares her list (followed by children sharing theirs if this is a family session).

5. Embrace New Memories!

Exchange lists and tear them up! Philippians 3:13 says, *"...forgetting what lies behind and pressing forward to what lies ahead."*

Start the "forgetting" process with a focus on this new memory of forgiveness as lists are exchanged and destroyed. (Some people burn or bury them!)

Additional suggestion: Hold hands and pray (even silently), thanking God for His forgiving you, changing you and healing your marriage and family.

6. Establish A New Habit!

"Let not the sun go down on your anger" (Ephesians 4:26). Confession to God and others we hurt along with forgiving others who have hurt us must become a daily habit if intimacy is to be maintained, otherwise your "emotional cup" will again be filled with hurtful emotions.

Questions
For Interaction

Incorporate these questions in your upcoming Marriage Staff Meetings

- Where did you live between the ages of 6 and 12?
- What person or place was the center of emotional warmth or security for you in early life?
- When, if ever did God become more than just a word to you? When did He become a living person to you?
- What is the most exciting thing going on in your life at present?
- If you could arrange things any way you wanted them, what would you change?
- Do inside or outside forces cause you the most trouble?
- What four words would you use to describe yourself? Which one is best?
- What word would you like others to use to describe you?
- What questions would you most like to ask God?
- Whose approval is most important to you?
- What age would you prefer to be and why?
- Are you more like your mother or father?
- Name two qualities you like best about yourself.
- Name two qualities you do not like about yourself.
- Jesus Christ thinks that I am _____.
- Write down a quality that you like about your spouse. Share.
- What is the best thing that has ever happened to you?
- What is the worst thing that has ever happened to you?
- Love means _____.
- What is, or was, your nickname and why?

Chapter Five

Affair-Proof
Your Marriage

Phil and Susy's Journey

The man who discipled me was far from perfect, and yet he is one of the most godly men I've ever known. I could say the same about my spiritual grandfather, Dave, and my spiritual great-grandfather, Joe. A common characteristic each of these men share is a growing, honest, intimate relationship with their wives. It seems to be a common denominator among most men who are used greatly in God's kingdom. Obviously, none of these marriages is perfect, but each exhibited a firm foundation of security that served as a powerful example to Susy and me.

As young Christians, Susy and I were discipled by godly believers; me by a physician named Jim, and Susy by a woman named Liane. Jim and his wife, Mary Gail, were so close to one another that I felt totally comfortable calling Mary Gail and leaving her a detailed message about what was going on in my life. As Liane, Jim, and Mary Gail parented us, they were transparent about their problems, pressures and failures. They didn't simply teach us the Scripture, they also lived their lives honestly and openly before us. Through their example, we learned many valuable lessons as to how to affair-proof our marriage.

Guard Your Marriage With Love

As I reflect back on the example of these godly marriages, I am drawn to a passage of Scripture that I have poured over many times through the years - 1 Corinthians 13. Various times in my marriage, I've had to focus directly on the principles in this Scripture, and at times, I've even carried 3x5 cards with each of the characteristics of love written out with a "performance box" next to it. At the top of the card, I write two questions: "Does this quality characterize my relationship with my wife?" And, "Was this quality evident in my life today as I interacted with Susy?"

As Susy and I exhibit mutual giving—"*…honor one another above yourselves*" (Romans 12:10),—we find our marriage not only strengthened and enriched but somehow guarded and protected.

In Paul's definition of love, he gives us seven things to do (commissions) and eight things to avoid (omissions).

Things To Do - Love Is…

- **Patient.** Have I been patient in my marriage today? Why am I in a hurry when the Lord has promised me sufficient time to accomplish all He wants me to do (without compromising my marriage)? Why do I sometimes show total strangers more patience than I do my wife who has devoted her life to me?
- **Kind.** Have I been kind today? Susy doesn't care if I'm rich, famous, muscular, or perfect, but Susy has a right to expect me to be nice to her.
- **Rejoices at right.** Oh Lord, help me to focus on our blessings and not complain (Philippians 2:14).
- **Bears all things.** With Christ's help (Philippians 4:13), there is no challenge that comes my way that I cannot overcome.
- **Believes all things.** The Lord has given us confidence that He has a great plan for our lives and He will reveal it in Scripture. Also, do I believe in Susy's hopes and dreams? Am I supportive of her daily activities?
- **Hopes all things.** Through our suffering, He has given us endurance; through endurance He has given us character; through His character, He has given us His hope (Romans 5:1).
- **Endures all things.** When I think Susy has wronged me, I'm tempted to defend my "rights." But then I remember that I am to endure all things. With the Lord's grace, forgiveness, and help, we do have the ability to endure all things in our marriage.

Things To Avoid - Love Is…

- **Not jealous.** Why do I focus on others, instead of focusing on Him, and let that affect my relationship with my wife?

- **Not boastful.** Why am I so proud of myself when I'm really nobody without His loving grace in my life?

- **Not arrogant.** Why can't I learn from the humbling circumstances God has allowed in my life?

- **Not rude.** Lord, forgive me for not exercising control over my tongue.

- **Not insistent on its own way.** Jesus called me to serve, not to seek a position of authority. Am I willing to serve my wife and meet her needs?

- **Not irritable.** My irritability is usually caused by uncertainty, and the loss of control, or to put it another way, fear. He gave me not the spirit of fear, but a spirit of power, love, and self-control (2 Timothy 1:7).

- **Not resentful.** My resentment is, in reality, discomfort with God's plan for me. Why should I question Almighty God's plan for me?

- **Does not rejoice at wrong.** Oh Lord, help me to be compassionate and not competitive, concerned for others and not eager to build myself up (Philippians 2:3).

Guard Your Marriage With Healing

When Susy and I have a disagreement, we try to quickly resolve the dispute with confession, repentance and forgiveness. But years ago, I would use one of several "substitutes" for confession, which were not only ineffective, but caused further harm to our relationship.

- **Ignore the problem.** This is where you "move on with a smile" as if there were no problem, leaving the issues undealt with and allowing the pain and hurt to fester.

- **Give an incomplete apology.** "Gee, Susy, I'm sorry. Let's hug, make up and move on."

- **Offer a "loaded confession."** "Honey, I'm really sorry, but if you had been on time I wouldn't have been rude."

- **Confess the sin but ignore the pain.** "Susy, I'm really sorry for my conduct. It was wrong of me to be rude to you, would you please forgive me?"

All along, Susy needed to hear a complete, appropriate apology.

"Susy, I'm very sorry I hurt you. What I did was wrong and I am really sorry for the pain caused by my rude abruptness with you on our way to the picnic. I will be more careful to trust the Lord with my schedule and not take it out on you."

In addition to our weekly dates, Susy and I find a real need to get off for longer periods of time, for a one-on-one evaluation of where we are, where we've been, and where we're going. It's during these meetings that God really works in our lives in a deep and decisive way. In your business, would you ever consider managing a department of salespersons and never have sales meetings? Why should we fail to meet with the one who has invested more in us than anyone else on earth, outside of our Lord and perhaps our parents? This is why weekly Marriage Staff Meetings are so important, plus other times of "getting away."

Guard Your Marriage With Purity

Sexual sin is so pervasive among men because of unguarded hearts. In working with men through the years, I have noticed some common reasons why men fall into sexual immorality:

Secret Sins

Many men have developed secret habits that run deep and even continue after salvation. Although delivered from the power of sin, these men continue to indulge in pornography and other sins that would lead them to greater moral failure. A surprising number of Christian men follow the pattern of Dan who, although he never technically broke his marriage vows through adultery, entertained a thought life that was divisive, destructive, and sinful. His thoughts went beyond momentary attractions or lustful thoughts to include fantasizing about women he met in business or saw in magazines. After years of harboring guilt and frustration, Dan came clean and confessed his destructive habit to his small accountability group. Dan was so disciplined in every other area of his Christian life that the men were shocked that he was so susceptible to immorality. They gathered around him, prayed for him and kept him accountable to the Lord and his wife in thought, word and deed. The great breakthrough for Dan was when his accountability group helped him make good on his promise to tell his wife about his problem. Sarah was first shocked, then relieved to understand why he was "increasingly distant" and finally she was able to forgive him, and appreciate his transparency and honest repentance. Through Dan's brokenness and resulting humility, Sarah found a more tender, open and honest husband whom she could help. Dan agreed with his wife and accountability group to make the same vow that Job made in Job 31:1.

No fear of God

Carl was a mechanical engineer who testified as a forensic expert witness in construction cases. His life around the office was one of leadership, respect, and example. His home life was relatively harmonious, except that he avoided one-on-one time with his wife and children. He was also well respected in the community. But on the road, he lived a secret life after 8:00 p.m. After a tough day of work, he would go to his hotel and engage in various types of pornography. It was on Good Friday when the cross-examining defense counsel, seeking to impeach Carl's testimony in a case, showed all of Carl's hotel bills to the jury. The plaintiff's counsel objected to the introduction of inadmissible and irrelevant testimony, but the defense counsel persisted by pointing out that the hotel charges were included in the plaintiff's claim for damages. Furthermore, he wanted to show the jury that Carl, as an expert, was not credible or trustworthy. The judge bought the argument and ruled the evidence admissible, at which point the defense counsel paraded in front of the entire courtroom, Carl's hotel bills which were riddled with area code 900 sex call charges and pay TV billings! The defense counsel was even prepared to prove, by hotel records, the titles and subject matter of the various movies charged to his account.

Who do we think we're kidding when we think we can hide from God? He is omniscient and omnipresent, as well as perfectly just. God loves us and our purity a lot more than our reputation, so He will often bring ruin to our reputation, exposing our secret lives. In the Old Testament, God often annihilated entire cities because of their sin. What makes us think that He will ignore ours? Carl's testimony was discredited, his reputation destroyed, and his marriage of 10 years devastated.

One of the greatest values of the Lord's ministry through David and Teresa Ferguson and their marriage intimacy seminars is that Christians are encouraged to get into small group Bible studies and accountability groups to delve into their weaknesses and failures from a biblical point of view, and to knead into their lives, godly solutions to the problems that create barriers, break-ups and broken lives.

An unbiblical view of sin, or, "It isn't so bad considering all the things I do well."

Some men think that God grades on the curve. That is, if I'm not as bad as other people, I must be OK. This lie has kept many from salvation and has prevented many Christians from experiencing the victorious life.

Jason was a senior vice president who managed the department of human resources for his manufacturing company in the Midwest. Jason was active in his church and community, and had a wonderful family. However, Jason always preferred to teach large Sunday School classes and speak to large groups of people; he avoided, like the plague, one-on-one discipleship.

True discipleship is analogous to parenting, as Paul indicated in 1 Thessalonians 2:7-8: *"We were gentle among you, like a mother caring for her little children. We loved you so much that we were delighted to share with you not only the gospel of God but our lives as well, because you had become so dear to us."*

One-on-one discipleship is not only the most effective tool to bring about change in individuals, but it is the method that God chose to bring about His kingdom (Matthew 28:19-20). Furthermore, discipleship is probably the best means of accountability a man can have. However, even in that setting a man must be honest with the one he's meeting with. I have found that if men will lie to God and to themselves, they also will lie to other men.

> *Christians are encouraged to get into small group Bible studies and accountability groups to delve into their weaknesses and failures from a biblical point of view.*

This one-on-one discipleship was missing in Jason's life. He destroyed his marriage, not by having an affair, or engaging in pornography, but by giving away his affections and attention to those with whom he worked and counseled in his company. Jason was extremely effective in building teams, but in his textile manufacturing facility, they were primarily composed of women. He counseled his female co-workers about their marriages, children, social and love lives, and their workplace pressures. Jason swore he never touched another woman, but he periodically and consistently gave away his heart, affection, and interest to other women. It wasn't really until his wife confronted him with her great need for encouragement, attention, and affection that Jason realized the extent to which he had damaged their marriage. Unfortunately, his situation was seemingly out of control. His wife Jean also worked for a large company and in her sales department she was surrounded by men who were impressed with her business acumen, gentle spirit and dogged determination. Jean got all the approval and attention she wanted - at work. She eventually had an affair with one of the men who reported to her. "The last thing I ever wanted was to be unfaithful to you!" were Jean's words, but she found her colleague's affection seemingly irresistible. Both Jason and Jean sinned against God and one another; Jason by being neglectful, Jean by being unfaithful.

Most of us grew up in an era where the mom stayed home and the dad worked. But that era ended with Norman Rockwell. We live in the 90's when many women are in the workplace and they to have to deal with all the corresponding pressures and temptations. Perhaps the greatest temptations come when their basic needs (such as attention, approval, acceptance, and affection) are met in the workplace when they should be met at home. Jason never went to bed with a woman other than his wife, but he sacrificed the sanctity of his marriage one conversation at a time over a period of about five years.

Thou shalt not steal

In my working with men around the country, I find a surprising number who must have watched too many reruns of the old TV show, *The Fugitive*. These men have a fascination with the daring, the offbeat, the high risk venture. Some of these men satisfy their desire for danger through risky business ventures or investments, but some men choose to fulfill this desire by flirting with "forbidden fruit"—they're fascinated with stealing someone else's wife.

Generally speaking, men don't read romance novels. But Trent did. He got into the habit of reading them on his daily train ride to work. Trent had grown up on the poor side of town and somewhere along the way, he believed the lie that it was OK to take from the "rich guys" as long as he didn't get caught. As a child, he got into the habit of stealing and as a teenager he was jailed for using drugs. When he came to Christ, he laid on the altar his lust for money, drugs and power, and five years later was even active in ministry as a layman. He spoke to large groups and shared his testimony of how he was delivered from a life of crime and despair and delivered into God's kingdom through salvation by faith. But he never dealt with the root of evil in his life. Although he had a beautiful wife and three married daughters, he set upon a course of conduct in his office of subtle, then overt, sexual harassment. As a career consultant in Christian ministry, Trent had many closed-door, confidential meetings with his secretaries and staff. One by one, they would quit after only a few months of working with Trent. His wife noticed the revolving door in his office, with young females coming and going. Then one Saturday afternoon, Anthony, the husband of Trent's secretary, after almost breaking down Trent's door, accused him of assaulting his wife. It was only through the quick action of one of the neighbors that Anthony was kept from ripping Trent limb from limb. He was totally enraged by his wife sharing the episodes of the sexual harassment and physical assaults she had endured working for Trent. One accuser's testimony might have been discredited, but seven other employees came forward with similar stories. It wasn't until halfway through the court case, brought by the women suing for damages, that Trent finally confessed to his sinful and unlawful conduct. Trent never overcame his temptation to steal that which was not his, and it almost destroyed his life.

Greed

Solomon had a thousand wives and concubines. Obviously, he didn't need that many wives; he just had this thing about having "the most." He was known for having the most wisdom, the most money, the most horses, and perhaps it was that same greed that drove him to have the most wives and concubines.

Tim was just such a man who needed more than anybody else. He didn't set his salary goals based on what he was worth, he just wanted to make more than the guy next door. He didn't care about close relationships with his children, he just wanted them to be the most involved and recognized kids in school. He didn't care about having deeply committed and moral friends, he just wanted to impress everyone in town. His desire for "just one more" led him to a pattern of unfaithfulness in his marriage, and it was only after he lost his wife that he realized he destroyed the one person who loved him for who he was as opposed to who he knew and what he had. Greed is a killer of the Christian life.

Escape

Some men are unhappy with their circumstances and attempt to escape in various ways. In Judges 4 there is an account of a man named Sisera who was fleeing the Lord's army. Seeking escape, he mistakenly went to the tent of Jael, a Kenite woman whom he did not realize was loyal to Israel. Feeling secure in his escape, he was even able to sleep in the comfort and security of her tent. While asleep, Jael *"drove the peg through his temple into the ground, and he died"* (Judges 4:21)!

Men often try to escape the discipline of the Lord and when they do they fall into tremendous pain and destruction. Patterns of anxiety and fear in a person's life can drive us to do the unimaginable. One of my prayers for purity in my own life is that if I ever dishonor the Lord, my wife and family by sinning with another woman, that three things would happen to me: (1) everyone in the world I know would find out about it the next day, (2) I would contract every known disease possible from such a moral failure, and (3) I would wake up afterwards with a tent peg through my temple. The Lord has said our hearts are wicked and deceitful, and our desire to walk in purity must be accompanied by a reminder of the fact that God hates sin, there is no "safe tent," the eternal impact is never worth a moment of pleasure, and we shouldn't be fooled by the "just this once" lie of Satan.

David and Teresa's Reflections

Guard Your Marriage By Meeting Needs

Surveys consistently indicate that marital affairs are not primarily sexually motivated. The pain and guilt of sexual infidelity usually come as an acquaintance develops into a "friendship," emotional bonding is added, and flirtation and temptation follow. The typical "attraction" is built not so much around the physical but the emotional. Significant emotional needs in the marriage are perceived as "unmet" and thus a vulnerability develops.

Recall our previous marital "truth:" Basic Needs Unmet = Frustration. Frustration leads to vulnerability and vulnerability can develop into an affair. Therefore it's important to understand your spouse's emotional-relational needs. With these needs "abundantly" met, your marriage is much more "affair-proofed."

Perhaps the most common justification for marital affairs is: "My wife (husband) and I don't ever talk any more. I was just looking for some companionship."

This comment indicates that there are significant unmet needs in the relationship. For example, "We don't talk anymore" might really mean I'm needing attention, understanding or empathy. "Looking for companionship" might reveal unmet needs for support, appreciation, acceptance, or affection. It's our premise that when these significant emotional-relational needs are met, a spouse is much less vulnerable to other "companionships."

As a role model of the relationship between Christ and the church, marriage is to portray a relationship built on giving to meet needs. Ephesians 5 speaks of Christ loving the church as He "gave Himself." There's great fulfillment in giving oneself in sharing the comfort, love and acceptance God has first given. As valid needs are met in the life of your spouse, marital intimacy and satisfaction are deepened.

Intimate Encounters - Key to Marital Closeness

Intimacy is developed and deepened as couples share experiences which draw them together. Intimacy doesn't just "happen" without effort but neither can it be "programmed" to happen. Couples seem to grow in closeness, for example, as they "encounter" one another spiritually, emotionally and physically. Such an encounter might be an ecstatic moment of common joy, a tearful sharing of genuine apology or an affectionate embrace. These intimate encounters help deepen marital closeness.

Intimate Encounters Include Three Dimensions—Spirit, Soul and Body

Spiritual encounters might include quiet prayer together or working together on a mission project. (Two developing genuine fellowship.) "Soulish" or "friendship" encounters involve the mind, emotions and will–as thoughts and dreams are shared, feelings are mutually expressed and common interests developed. (Two becoming best friends.) Physical encounters involve caring touch, affectionate embrace and passionate union. (Two becoming affectionate "lovers.")

Intimate Encounters Involve Four Ingredients

These four ingredients present a sound "strategy" for developing intimacy.

- **Affectionate Caring** –"I care for you." I want to know you; I'll be there when you need me—because I care for you.
- **Vulnerable Communication** – "I trust you." I am willing to vulnerably share with you my pain, fears, weaknesses, thoughts, dreams and aspirations—because I trust you.
- **Joint Accomplishment** – "I need you." I can't do it without you, and I love it when we do things together—because I need you.
- **Mutual Giving** – "I love you." I think more highly of you than I do myself; I want to meet your needs—because I love you.

A committed and sensitive partner will seek to abundantly give to his or her spouse's needs...not out of fear but out of the abundance of God's gracious provision. Happy need meeting!

Taken Captive
By His Love
2 Corinthians 5:14

The fall of the Berlin Wall, capitalism thriving in the former USSR, and communism in retreat evidence the pursuit of freedom and the cry for liberty. We don't have to look far however, to find contradictions in this cry for liberty. Each day brings more controversy over rights and freedoms— parental rights versus children's rights, states' rights versus national priorities, freedom of choice versus pro-life, discrimination versus reverse discrimination, freedom from moral decay versus freedom of expression, right to die versus personal responsibility. Our fast paced and media driven culture has seemingly brainwashed us into demanding our freedom at any cost.

The Paradox of Freedom

We can easily miss the biblical paradox of freedom. Christ often spoke of the paradoxical nature of His kingdom—lose your life and find it (Matthew 16:25), love those who despise you (Matthew 5:44), and die in order to bear fruit (John 12:24) but perhaps the greatest biblical paradox concerns "freedom." The paradoxical message is presented in various settings and uses a variety of analogies, but the message seems clear: surrender to God's Spirit, God's Son, and God's love and you'll experience true freedom: *"Where the Spirit of the Lord is, there is liberty"* (2 Corinthians 3:17), *"So if the Son sets you free, you will be free indeed"* (John 8:36).

In one of the most insightful passages on this paradox, we find Christ sharing the truth of finding true rest, *"Take my yoke upon you and learn from Me"* (Matthew 11:29-30). Submitting to His yoke brings blessing! Somehow our "yielding" brings liberty as His yoke is easy and light. Captivity brings true freedom!

> *"So if the Son sets you free, you will be free indeed"*
> *(John 8:36).*

Held Captive By Something

Scripture is filled with references to the pervasiveness of our captivity. As non-believers we once *"Followed the ways of this world and...the ruler of the kingdom of the air..."* (Ephesians 2:2). The Greek word "sunecho" used in 2 Corinthians 5:14 to describe the "captivating," constraining love of Christ, is also used to describe being held captive by fear (Luke 8:37), by the crowd (Luke 8:45), and by enemies (Luke 19:43). Paul uses the same word to describe being *"torn between the two"* as he shares the dilemma of wanting to be with Christ yet remaining with the Philippians (Philippians 1:23). It seems that "captivity" is inevitable! But by God's grace we can choose our master! Will it be fear, the crowd, enemies, the course of this world, or will it be the constraining love of Christ?

> *...we can choose our master! Will it be fear, the crowd, enemies, the course of this world, or will it be the constraining love of Christ?*

Study Questions

Pause and reflect on some areas of past "captivity" in which you now experience freedom...

_____

_____

What heart felt emotions do you have for these areas of liberation?

_____

_____

Captivating Love is to be Experienced

Captivity is not an intellectual exercise or mental process. It is first and foremost experiential truth, an experienced reality that impacts one's total being. It's more than seeking to mentally comprehend the vastness of God's love only to be frustrated by our finiteness. So it is with the constraining love of Christ. It's more than choosing to tell others about this great love, as significant as this is. So what does it mean to be constrained by His love? To better understand

and experience such constraint is to better comprehend true love—as an issue of God's heart and nature rather than only an issue of rational truth. The declaration that *"love is from God"* (1 John 4:7) is a certain and secure rational truth but to personally experience that this love was *"manifest in us...that God sent His Son to be the propitiation for our sins"* (1 John 4:9-10) makes it an issue of relationship, an emotional issue of the heart. As a believer in Christ, I am, have been, and always will be loved by my Creator. How will my heart respond? To explore this issue is to explore experiencing His constraining love.

The Greek word "sunecho"(to be captivated) also gives insight into the fullness of this constraint. The word seems to describe the believer's heart response to the Father's unbounded love. The word is often translated "to hold," "to secure," "to control or empower." Could it be that:

- thanksgiving for His unmerited love **holds** me in grateful obedience, freeing me from the pull of my sinful nature;
- praise for His loving character **reminds** me of my secure future, freeing me from the fear of losing His love;
- worship of the God "who is love," **empowers** my grateful stewardship of His love, freeing me from selfish preoccupation.

Notice that thanksgiving, praise and worship are not merely passive intellectual musings but experiences of the heart and spirit! Write words of...

thanksgiving,

_____

_____

praise,

_____

_____

and worship,

_____

_____

Experiences of Captivating Love

It's His love that is constraining, motivating and empowering. Therefore, we should find evidences of this divine love lived out in our lives.

- His love **initiates**—it moves first, never waiting around to be asked or invited! *"There is no one who seeks for God!"* (Romans 3:11), but rather, *"He came to seek and to save"* (Luke 19:10). Initiate, initiate, initiate toward those God has called you to love!

- His love **sacrifices**—it's free but it's not cheap; it cost His Son. *"God so loved the world that He gave"* (John 3:16). *"As Christ loved the church and gave Himself up for her"* (Ephesians 5:25). Sacrifice a little of your time, convenience, and self-interest in communicating His love toward others.

- His love **rejoices**—it gives with gladness, thrilled at the opportunity to care for others. *"And when he finds it (the lost sheep), he joyfully puts it on his shoulders..."* (Luke 15:5). *"Selling their possessions and goods, they gave to anyone as he had need...with glad and sincere hearts"* (Acts 2:45-46). Rejoice often over the privilege of giving. Reflect often on the wonder of having something of eternal significance to share.

In an age filled with "knowing" about truth, rather than experiencing it, take particular note of the relational and experiential nature of His constraining love which initiates, sacrifices, and rejoices!

Study Questions

> *Rejoice often over the privilege of giving.*

What "initiative" could I lovingly demonstrate toward my spouse?

_____

_____

What loving sacrifice could I make to bless my spouse?

_____

_____

What are a few ways my spouse brings rejoicing to my heart?

_____

_____

_____

Meeting Your
Spouse's Needs

Husbands, Minister to Your Wife's Need for Security

Security is often defined as "freedom from threats of danger or pain; to be safe and certain and sure of one's safety." The key issue in meeting a wife's need for security is to remove her fears. For instance, a wife who fears that her husband's work is more important than she is, might feel insecure. A wife who fears that her husband is not totally committed to marriage fidelity or permanence will naturally feel threatened or jealous. Countless fears will inevitably arise over the course of a marriage relationship and a loving husband will be actively involved in helping remove them, thus building a more secure relationship.

Husbands, complete the following exercise with your wife. As she shares, listen attentively and reassure her that you care.

Biblical Reflections

> *"For God did not give us a spirit of timidity"* (2 Timothy 1:7).
> *"But perfect love drives out fear"* (1 John 4:19).
> *"Husbands, love your wives, just as Christ loved the church"*
> (Ephesians 5:25).

Better Understanding Her Need for Security

Noted below are several ideas to help deepen the sense of security in a marriage. Ask your wife to make two lists for you:

■ I'd love for your top 5 priorities to be:

1.

2.

3.

4.

5.

I often feel your top 5 priorities are:

1.

2.

3.

4.

5.

- **When you sense your wife's fears or insecurities, share** – "I can sense you're feeling fearful and I want you to know I'm committed to reassure you...I want to help drive out your fears."

- **Ask about her fears** – "Honey, could you share with me some of the things that you've recently been worrying about or fearing? I'd like to work on helping you with them."

- **Ask your wife how you can increase her sense of security** – "What could I do to help you feel more secure in our relationship? I really want to help."

- **Have weekly Marriage Staff Meetings** – Make it a priority to schedule a "talk" time with your wife each week (1 to 1-1/2 hours) to discuss plans, schedules, children, family needs and anything else your wife would like to discuss. This time helps a wife feel more secure that she and the family are indeed very important.

- **Regularly schedule "dates"** – Schedule times when you and your spouse are doing something alone, just for fun; without children (that's family time) without friends (that's social time). These dates give a wife something to look forward to; a husband initiating the plans helps her feel secure in his leadership.

- **Make 30 second phone calls** – "Hi, Sweetheart. I was just thinking about you and wanted to call to check on you. I love you and look forward to seeing you tonight." This communicates an important emotional message that says, "Even though I'm working a lot and very busy...I'm thinking of you!"

- **Engage in vulnerable accountability** – Ask your wife: "What are some things I've been doing recently that irritate you? I want to work on changing some of them." Listen attentively without being defensive; pray about what is shared and then implement needed changes. A willingness to consider a wife's "wishes" for change helps communicate your priority of her.

Wives, Minister to Your Husband's Need to be Honored

Honoring your husband means to value him as an especially meaningful person in your life...your personal "hero." It also includes honoring his wishes as you are sensitive in desiring to please him and honoring his decisions as you free him to lovingly lead you. Honoring your husband is a special ministry of love that requires a deepened work of faith.

Wives, complete the following exercise *with your husband*. As he shares, listen attentively and reassure him that you care.

Biblical Reflections

- *"...like Sarah, who obeyed Abraham and called him her master. You are her daughters"* (1 Peter 3:6).
- *"Be devoted to one another...give preference to one another in honor"* (Romans 12:10).

Better Understanding His Need To Be Honored

Listed below are several ideas to help deepen your husband's sense of being honored.

- List below six areas of "strength" or positive character qualities you see in your husband.

  1.

  2.

  3.

  4.

  5.

  6.

Now practice communicating your appreciation for these six items: (1) verbally when you're alone, (2) "publicly" when you're with others or (3) in writing by a special love note.

- **Ask about "wishes"** – "Honey, I honestly want to better honor you as my husband...particularly in seeking to meet more of your special "wishes." Would you share with me some "wishes" that I could help fulfill?"

- **Talk about "decisions"** – "As I come to realize how much I need and value your leadership, I want to become more sensitive not to criticize or resist your decisions. Can you share with me decisions in which you'd appreciate more support?"

- **Make him "King For A Day"** – Schedule a surprise day focused on giving just to him; maybe breakfast in bed; a special card, favorite outing, favorite friends over or just quiet "togetherness"...be creative and even romantic!

- **Brag and don't compare** – Emphasize his strengths and communicate appreciation; don't tease him or attack him through comparisons with other men . . . co-workers, fathers, brothers, pastors, etc.

- **Don't sweat the small stuff!** – Back off and let him make decisions and even mistakes; let him miss an exit off the expressway or pick a restaurant with a long waiting line; let him verbalize "wild" ideas without shooting them down!

- **"Date" him again** – Return to some of the little things he enjoyed while dating; sit by him, hold his hand, use his favorite perfume or special sleepwear, play "our song," etc. (Most men haven't grown out of these wishes!)

- **Be honest about your passive-aggressiveness** – What are some things you know he enjoys but withhold from him when you're angry? This inventory usually reminds you that you already know many of his wishes...the issue then becomes putting away anger (Ephesians 4:31-32) so you can be free to unconditionally love him.

Three Practical Ways to Help "Affair-Proof" Your Marriage

Couple Prayer Times

One recent survey indicated fewer than 15% of church-going couples pray together. Most of the reasons are obvious:

- I'm not exactly sure what to say.
- I would not pray "as good" as the Preacher.
- I might get corrected by my spouse!
  ...and the list of excuses goes on...

One simple recommendation is this:

Spend a few minutes talking about "things that matter"
- ...concerns, hopes, dreams or fears
- ...kids, work, money, feelings, or future events. (This might come at the close of a Marriage Staff Meeting or during the last minutes before sleep.)

Reach over and take one another by the hand (a husband's initiative here as "leader" seems appropriate). Pray together silently for 2 or 3 minutes (if you become comfortable praying out loud, fine and if not, fine). You'll sense an important spiritual closeness to one another and you may also find that emotional and physical closeness often follow.

Sharing Emotions

Each of us experience emotions. Some share their feelings openly while others hide them. Some seem overly sensitive to emotion, while others are unsure of what they feel. The same emotion can be expressed in greatly differing ways. For instance, loneliness in some might be expressed with sad withdrawal, while with others, it might be expressed through endless conversation. A major ingredient in relational closeness is the open and constructive expression of emotion. The first step is to develop an emotional "vocabulary." To encourage emotional sharing in your marriage, take turns naming as many emotions as you can.

Why is it important to identify emotions? One reason is that many times, emotions define for us major emotional needs: feeling unappreciated means we need appreciation; feeling rejected implies needing acceptance and feeling misunderstood implies the need for understanding.

Together, list at least ten positive emotions (excited, hopeful, etc.) and ten painful emotions (lonely, rejected). Then take turns sharing recent events in your lives and the emotions they invoked. For instance, often, a person might identify anger as a felt emotion, but in reality this anger might be the "sum" of feeling unappreciated, rejected and misunderstood.

Marriage and Family Goal Setting

Without a Vision, People Perish – Proverbs 29:18

Every marriage needs a vision — a sense of direction and destiny; a guiding framework around which we can make decisions and distinct objectives toward which we can stretch.

Using the "exploratory" questions below, discuss each item and begin to identify specific goals you'd like to see accomplished:

- In what two key ways would you like to see me grow personally in the next year?
- How would you most like me to pray for you in the next few months?
- What is a recurring concern you may have about each of our children?
- What is an important item you'd like to see emphasized in our romance?
- What do you see as two of the most important challenges we may face this year?
- What improvements or changes would you most like to see around our home?

Blessed are Those Who Mourn

Phil and Susy's Journey

Because of the childhood pain I experienced, I developed a deep sense of loneliness and insecurity. On two occasions, mom spent several months in a mental institution which left my older sister and me to fend for ourselves - alone. My sister tried to take care of me the best she could, but she was also dealing with her own feelings of rejection and hurt. She was in a more difficult position than I was because she was in high school and her friends were more generally aware of our family's problems. My three best friends, Steve, Ted and Jimmy, nicknamed me "Pruner" which made me want to vomit every time I heard it.

By and large, I had to deal with my pain alone. As my trauma at home increased, my friends were embarrassed, our neighbors were shocked, my dad was busy at work, and no one from our church ever reached out to us. But there was one person who I know cared about me, understood my pain and accepted me for who I was— Mrs. McKay, my next door neighbor. She had even caught me doing a lot of bad stuff but genuinely forgave me. I never knew if she figured out that I was the one who cremated a dead cat in her incinerator, egged her house on Halloween, and raided her garage for pine boards for boats; but regardless, she always seemed to care. I always sensed her love and concern, often while I devoured another piece of her fabulous home-made pie.

I don't remember if she went to church or not and we never discussed religion, but as an accomplished opera singer she had gotten her start singing hymns in the church. Mrs. McKay loved and cared for me during the most difficult time of my life.

Several years ago I talked with Mrs. McKay and shared with her how much she had meant to me and how I had found the ultimate cure for the pain, insecurity, anger and bitterness that I had developed as a boy. As I sat in her home, I shared how I came to Christ and then asked her if she would like to go through the gospel tract called "Steps to Peace with God." She said she would. As we went through the Scripture, she would finish verses I had started to quote. When I looked surprised she said, "Well, I played piano in church when I was a child." She was then well into her 80's. When we got to the end of the presentation of the gospel, she said she wanted to pray to receive Jesus Christ as her Lord and Savior, and to my absolute delight I had the incredible privilege of leading Mrs. McKay to Christ.

I'll always have a special place in my heart for Mrs. McKay because she was the only one who mourned with me as a child when I was hurting. Of course, as a young boy, I didn't know that what she was doing was technically called "mourning," but it sure felt good. She simply allowed me to verbalize my hurt, frustration and anxiety and then she responded with kind, gentle words. She didn't try to lecture me, and thank goodness, she never said, "Phil, big boys don't cry." Whenever I left her house I felt comforted, I felt good, I felt blessed and I was full of pie!

Years later, I discovered what was going on in those meetings between a kind lady and the neighborhood brat—Matthew 5:4, *"Blessed are those who mourn, for they shall be comforted."* I mourned, Mrs. McKay comforted me, and I left feeling blessed!

David and Teresa's Reflections

Mrs. McKay met a very significant need in Phil's life—the need for comfort. In this life, hurt and pain are inevitable and comfort is the solution.

Before we discuss in detail, the biblical principle of mourning and comforting, we need to discuss the principle of emotional responding - responding to emotions with emotions.

Emotional Closeness ...A Lost Ingredient

Our world seems to have emphasized achievement and performance to the exclusion of emotional development. Young children seem to do well learning to tie shoes and counting to ten but who helps them identify their feelings? School age children usually begin a treadmill of endless activities...scouts, dance, sports, piano...but how do they learn to deal with normal rejections, fears and disappointments? Adolescents often focus on athletics, academics, popularity or "crowd pleasing," but how are they healing their inevitable hurts?

Without developing an adequate feeling "vocabulary" or much emphasis on emotional sharing, adults often enter marriage hopeful of deep emotional closeness but ill-prepared to experience it. The friendship dimension of intimacy begins to suffer as feelings of love, romance and affection diminish. Without adequate emotional skills a couple copes the best they can, often content with just staying together. There's often a drifting apart into separate worlds—a husband absorbed in his business or hobbies; a wife escaping into the world of professions, "super mom" or endless activity. This drifting apart can bring further complications of increasing resentment, self-sufficiency and heightened fear of rejection or abandonment.

Spiritual Complications

For many couples, this "coping" existence is made even more tragic by its contrast with their religious expectations and hopes. Much pretending often takes place because what is observed at home is so different from the scriptural ideal proclaimed at church. Can I honestly be living a life which is *"thinking more highly of others"* (Philippians 3:2) and it not be making a dramatic impact at home with marriage and family? Can I genuinely be living consistent with the grace of my having been forgiven while at the same time harboring anger and bitterness toward a spouse or other family member (See Ephesians 4:31-32)? When a person's home life is dramatically different from their spiritual values and teachings, feelings of inadequacy, guilt and condemnation are often added to the previous pain of loneliness, rejection, fear, anger and bitterness.

Developing the Skill of Emotional Responding

At Intimate Life Ministries, we're often asked, particularly by men, "How can I get in touch with my emotions? Sometimes I feel emotionally 'numb' and I know that hinders my ability to relate to other people, particularly my wife." Our answer to that question is to explain what we call "emotional responding." Simply put, emotional responding means that when emotions are shared, an emotional response is required. When the response is one of logic or facts, criticism or complaint, intimacy is hindered and couples and families begin concluding "we just can't communicate!" An emotional need must be meet with an emotional response. Learning this seemingly simple but profound principle can greatly enhance our relationships. Emotional closeness is a major part of being "best friends" with a spouse and is obviously a significant ingredient in sexual intimacy as well. Emotional responding is learning to respond to another person's emotions. If your spouse, child or friend expresses an emotion, you need to answer him or her with an emotional response. It would sound something like: "I know you are hurting and I care; I know you have a need and I care."

This is often very difficult for us to do because:
- We may have never developed a feeling vocabulary.
- We won't let our hearts feel what our heads know.
- It is easier to answer emotions with unproductive responses.
- We have no idea what emotional responding looks or sounds like.

In order to enhance your marital relationship, let's take a look at these four hindrances and learn how to correct them.

First, develop a feeling vocabulary. (You started a list of emotions in Chapter 5. Try to expand this list.) You might then spend time sharing as a couple or as a family. Here is an example of what emotional sharing may sound like, "Today, I found myself feeling _____ when _____ happened." This will help you develop a feeling vocabulary.

Study Questions

Recently I found myself feeling (some positive emotion) when...

_____

_____

Recently I found myself feeling (some painful emotion) when...

_____

_____

In one sense, emotional responding is simply the experiencing of Romans 12:15: *"Rejoice with those who rejoice; mourn with those who mourn."* When you experienced the positive emotion noted on the previous page, did you share it with your spouse? Did they rejoice with you? When you experienced the painful emotion noted above, did you share it with your spouse? Did they mourn with you?

Second, learn to let your heart feel what your head knows. In order to experience abundance and intimacy we have to open up to feelings. As individuals, we are wired to think, feel and do. Many of us don't handle the feeling part well.

Remember that Jesus experienced emotion. In the Upper Room He wanted His joy to remain full in the disciples (John 15:11). He wept with Mary at Lazarus' death (John 11:35). In the garden he said, *"My soul is overwhelmed with sorrow..."* (Matthew 26:38). Jesus experienced emotions, but did not let them control Him. It is OK to experience emotions—that does not make you weak. Spend time meditating on the sufferings of Jesus (John 13:21, John 14:7-9, Matthew 26:38-39). Ask the Father to open your emotions as you enter into the "fellowship of Christ's sufferings" (Philippians 3:10). Coming to feel emotionally for your Savior will prepare you to feel for those whom He and you care for.

Third, emotion should always be answered with emotion. Many times we answer with "substitutes" and they never work. Some of those unproductive responses include:

- **Facts, logic and reasons** - Someone has just said some hurtful things to you. As you tell your husband about it, he responds, "Don't let what she says bother you. You know it's not true."
- **Criticism** - Or he responds, "You sure are sensitive. Why do you let her get to you so easily? You really need to toughen up."
- **Complaints** - "It sure was stupid to let all those people know how easily she gets to you. I found the whole thing embarrassing. If you keep this up we won't have any friends."
- **Neglect** - "Well, I sure hope you can work it out. It's not my problem."

Fourth, what does emotional responding look and sound like? It always includes understanding, empathy, gentleness, reassurance and confession if necessary. For instance, if your spouse is hurting, how does that make you feel? (sad, compassionate, etc.) Use those feeling words to communicate to him or her how it makes you feel to see your spouse hurting: "It saddens me to see you hurt because I care about you; I have compassion toward you when you hurt because I love you."

The chart below further explains the concept of emotional responding, illustrating the classic "unproductive" responses to emotional need or hurt. Such unproductive responses tend to be associated with unfulfilled or "unhealthy" relationships.

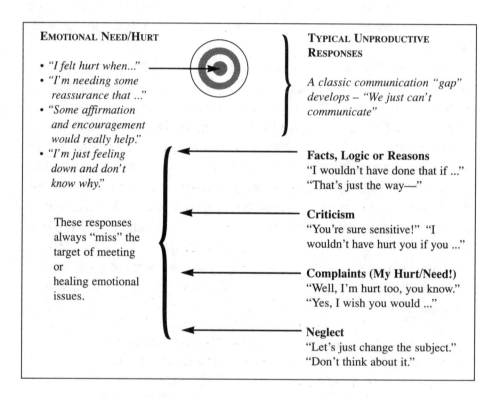

This chart illustrates *productive* responses to emotional need or hurt.

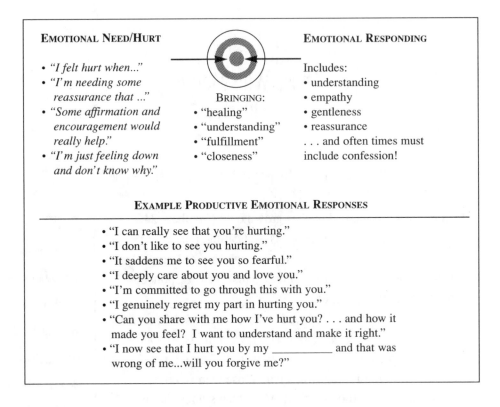

EMOTIONAL NEED/HURT

- *"I felt hurt when..."*
- *"I'm needing some reassurance that ..."*
- *"Some affirmation and encouragement would really help."*
- *"I'm just feeling down and don't know why."*

BRINGING:
- "healing"
- "understanding"
- "fulfillment"
- "closeness"

EMOTIONAL RESPONDING

Includes:
- understanding
- empathy
- gentleness
- reassurance
. . . and often times must include confession!

EXAMPLE PRODUCTIVE EMOTIONAL RESPONSES

- "I can really see that you're hurting."
- "I don't like to see you hurting."
- "It saddens me to see you so fearful."
- "I deeply care about you and love you."
- "I'm committed to go through this with you."
- "I genuinely regret my part in hurting you."
- "Can you share with me how I've hurt you? . . . and how it made you feel? I want to understand and make it right."
- "I now see that I hurt you by my _____ and that was wrong of me...will you forgive me?"

When we put emotional responding into practice we experience Matthew 5:4.

- A person is hurting - mourning.
- Someone comforts them - comfort.
- The hurting person receives - blessing, even when nothing external has changed. The thing that hurt may still be in place - but I'm "blessed" that you care! I'm not alone in my hurt!

Comfort is powerful. God tells us to *"mourn with those who mourn"* (Romans 12:15), *"...so that we can comfort those in any trouble with the comfort we ourselves have received from God"* (2 Corinthians 1:2-4), and that it is *"not good for man to be alone"* (Genesis 2:18). As we apply these scriptural principles to our lives, we will indeed experience the blessing of intimacy as our aloneness is removed through the caring involvement of others.

Mourn With Those Who Mourn - Romans 12:15

The Occasion of His Weeping - "When Jesus saw her weeping."

In a day when men's love has grown cold (Matthew 24:12), it's significant that we see Jesus as a caring, concerned friend. In a culture filled with the explosion of knowledge and technology, it's insightful to notice that Jesus responded emotionally to this situation.

Jesus was with those He loved. *"Jesus loved Martha and her sister (Mary) and Lazarus"* (John 11:5). Weeping is an appropriate response to a loved one who is in pain. When we rejoice with those who rejoice and weep with those who weep, love takes on an emotional dimension. More than simply "knowing" that we're loved, the emotional element allows us to experience "felt" love. For instance, a child may intellectually "know" that he is loved by his parents because they provide for him and protect him. But it's also important for the child to "feel" loved. Likewise, we know God loves us because He abundantly provides for us; but we more fully experience His felt love through His willingness to shed tears.

"When Jesus therefore saw her weeping and the Jews who came with her, also weeping, He was deeply moved in spirit and was troubled... Jesus wept" (John 11:33, 35).

This story also demonstrates Jesus' selfless caring. It was an occasion of sadness, loss, and grief that brought Christ's tears. But it was not primarily His loss, but others; not His grief, but Mary's. Shedding tears for another may be one of our most selfless acts of love—hurting that another is hurting; weeping that another weeps.

List other examples from the gospels when Jesus expressed comfort and compassion:

_____

_____

What does His example say about *your need* for comfort and compassion?

_____

_____

> *"He was deeply moved in spirit and was troubled."*

What does His example say about *your need to express* comfort and compassion?

_____

_____

The Example of Weeping

The gospels often speak of Christ being *"moved with compassion"* (Matthew 9:36, 15:32, Luke 15:20) - not just ready to give advice. A compassionate heart first communicates true care and concern: then, from the security of a care-filled relationship, advice, instruction and exhortation can be tenderly offered. The old cliche, "I don't care how much you know until I know how much you care!" is true. As Jesus weeps, we see an example of deep inward expression. Jesus' tears are an issue of the inner spirit, an expression of a troubled heart. Tears do not flow merely from man's intellect, right doctrine, or from a disciplined life of right living. Right "believing" and right "behaving," as critical and necessary as they are, will never be sufficient in expressing Christ-like gentleness, compassion and tender care. Tears are an issue of the heart.

Jesus also demonstrates vulnerable self-disclosure—"Jesus wept." The caring, troubled heart of the Savior is disclosed. There's no self-protection or hesitancy from fearing others' approval. Not only has He come to know Mary's pain (and ours), but He also reveals His own. Since man's fall in the Garden, he has hidden, worn the mask, and played the games. But the last Adam, Jesus, forsakes all games and masks - He reveals Himself as all man and all God.

Study Questions

Discuss the significance of the following statement: "Believing right and behaving right are essential to Christ-like living but not sufficient to fully express Great Commandment love."

_____

_____

Discuss what factors (childhood issues, cultural messages, or examples) might hinder your vulnerable self disclosure of comfort.

_____

_____

Consider 2 Corinthians 1:2-4 and realize that God, as the God of all comfort, has comforted you. How is your sharing comfort with others being a good steward of what you have received?

_____

_____

The Miracle of His Weeping

The crowd was amazed when the carpenter from Nazareth shouted with a loud voice, "Lazarus, come forth." And they were no doubt shocked when he did! What a mighty miracle - the rejected One from Nazareth raised the dead! But there were other miracles that day, perhaps less obvious but equally amazing.

Consider the miracle of God crying! Just as miraculous as a "man raising the dead" is a God who would cry. The Creator of the universe, the true God-man entered into the pain of an obscure family from Bethany—and cried. For every believer, there's the miracle of the empty tomb, but there's also the miracle of our great High Priest who can sympathize with us and enter into our sorrow. For every child of God, there's the sure promise of heaven but there's also the miracle of His daily attentive care, concern, and compassion.

The Miracle of Removing our "Aloneness"

Mary is no longer "alone" in her grief—the Savior has entered her world. Mary mourns the tragic loss of her brother but the Savior's tears bring comfort and blessing. *"Blessed are those who mourn for they shall be comforted"* (Matthew 5:4). But how can one feel blessed in the midst of grief, pain, loss, and mourning? As Christ's empathetic tears drive away Mary's aloneness, her pain subsides and her fear diminishes because of His love and concern. *"Perfect love casts out fear"* and there is no more perfect love than a God who cries for me and allows me to shed His tears for others. It is the wonder of "weeping with those who weep."

Study questions

> What impact do you experience emotionally as you meditate on the fact that Jesus is your Great High Priest, and that He hurts when you hurt and rejoices when you rejoice. How does that impact you emotionally?

_____

_____

Reflect on a time in your past when you received true comfort from spouse, friend or family members and write about how your pain was turned into a "blessing" (Matthew 5:4).

_____

_____

Delving Deeper Into The Three Dimensions of Intimacy

Spiritual Intimacy – Where to Start?

For most couples, physical oneness (sex) is relatively easy to "assess" or "count," emotional oneness more difficult to grasp, but spiritual oneness is almost too "vague" to even discuss. Is spiritual closeness simply attending the same church or sitting together in services? Is it having identical beliefs or using the same Bible?

Tragically, for many Christian couples, their individual spiritual life may be maturing but their spiritual closeness as a couple is more myth than reality. Here are some recommendations for improving spiritual closeness:

Where to Start Personally

Commit to one new spiritual goal.

Couple closeness is founded upon two individuals each getting closer to God only to find that they feel closer to one another. Sample goals:

- Read through the entire New Testament this year (one chapter a day will more than do it).
- Memorize 10 Scripture passages on communication (Ephesians 4:29, Proverbs 10:19, 12:18, 12:25, 15:1, 15:28, 16:23, 17:27, 19:13, 25:24).
- Establish a daily devotional time.
- Apply yourself to consistent Bible study. (See suggested resources at the end of this workbook.)

Where to Start as a Couple

There are two simple but effective ways to develop spiritual oneness:

- Pray together (see Praxis, Chapter 5).
- Read selected Bible verses and share insights. Choose a verse

(For example Matthew 6:33: *"Seek ye first the kingdom of God and His righteousness and all these things will be added unto you"*) and share what the verse means to you. Avoid criticism, arguments or giving "my answer is more spiritual than yours" responses.

"Again I tell you, that if two of you on earth agree about anything you ask for, it will be done for you by My Father in heaven" (Matthew 18:19). There's no more powerful "two" praying together than a husband and wife who, in God's eyes, are already one!

Emotional Intimacy—Where to Start!

Through Communication

Counselors often list as the top marital issues: communication, money, sex and kids! Although therapy may be needed to deal with deeper underlying issues such as insecurity, fear of rejection, resentments and childhood hurts...these top four issues are definitely common "presenting" or surface problems. The couple may see one or more of these issues as a major stress in the relationship.

Fundamental among these four is the issue of communication since it obviously greatly effects a couple's ability to deal with the other three (money, sex and kids). Each of us communicates not only through words, but also through actions, behavior, attitude and body language. Communication skills must be learned, improved and practiced.

There are several different types of communication:

- **Chit-chat** - Hi, how are you? How was your day? When's dinner?
- **Factual** - Johnny hit Susie today. Your car's out of gas. Do I have money in my account? I'm too tired tonight!
- **Intimate** - Freedom to share dreams, hopes, fears, feelings and concerns in an atmosphere of loving acceptance.

If the "pulse" of your marital communication is not as intimate as you would like, it is likely suffering from one of the following common hindrances to intimate communication.

- **Unavailable Spouse** - It takes quality time together to move past chit-chat (Thus the importance of Marriage Staff Meetings, Chapter 3.)
- **Unhealed Hurts** - Why talk intimately with someone I'm still mad at! (Thus the importance of Healing Marital Hurts, Chapter 4.)
- **Unbridled Tongue** - Speaking before you think often "wounds" other people.
- **Unproductive Criticism** - Being criticized quenches intimate talk.

Communication doesn't just happen! The most common divorce pleading is "incompatibility" — even for couples married 20 years or longer. Tragically it's possible to live in the same house, eat at the same table and sleep in the same bed, but not come to really know one another. As a beginning point, you need a Weekly Marriage Staff Meeting if you haven't already started this habit.

Physical Intimacy—Where to Start!

Improving the Quality!

Sex is often among the top four problems couples have and it's the "quantity" of sexual encounters that is the most frequent complaint. Tragically, couples have often come to define their sexual relationship in terms of numbers! How often do we have sex? How many times did one or the other reach orgasm? How much foreplay? How long does it last?

It's tragic to take God's designed plan for "two becoming one flesh" and reduce it to numbers. A fundamental error in marriage enrichment is to attempt to "negotiate" these numbers —comparing your sexual frequency with the "average" couple (whatever that is) or agreeing to "trade" two more sexual encounters per week for 20 more minutes of foreplay (or for one dinner date and cleaning out the garage!) Much more successful is the following approach:

Focus on Quality and Quantity Resolves Itself!

Here are some suggestions for improving the quality:
1. **Plan times together**—great stress and much anger comes from dashed expectations at the end of a long day when there's no mutual desire. (All of your sexual encounters should not be planned, but some should.)

- "Calendar" together some times during Marriage Staff Meetings
- Part in the morning with tenderness, touch and one of you expressing, "I'd sure like to be together with you tonight...let's plan on it!" (A big plus to arousal is anticipation; allowing yourself, through the day, to think of pleasant sexual times with your spouse.)
- Maybe it's time for: a night alone without kids, friends or other distractions; some unhurried lovemaking; a "coupon" special at a local hotel or trading out with a friend for overnight child care so you can be alone in your own house. (A good recommendation—one night alone for sexual rekindling each six months.)

2. **Add variety to your lovemaking**—sexual routine often produces boredom and disinterest. Consider the following:
   - Vary the "atmosphere" through changing locations or times of the day; change the lighting or use candles; change lingerie or use sexy nightwear; change powders, perfumes or aftershave; add music.
   - Vary the "routine" through changing sexual positions; change who initiates (trade off pleasuring one another); add a full body massage with baby oil or lotion; creatively be together other than in the bed!

3. **Communicate more openly**
   - Sexual intimacy can't be a guessing game; two physically different people with differing personalities, backgrounds, preferences and hang-ups must gradually learn to talk more openly about sexual oneness.
   - During a relaxing massage of one another, give feedback as to good and great feelings.
   - Read to one another portions of *The Song of Solomon.*

Emotional Responding

When someone is hurting, the only proper response is comfort. But we are often tempted to offer unproductive substitutes such as: logic/reasoning, advice/instruction, pep-talk, minimizing, personal fear/anxiety, or martyr's response. Review the following scenario below and discuss the six "unproductive responses" and the one "productive response." With each unproductive response, pause and reflect on how you might, at times, respond in this manner.

Setting

John and Suzanne have been married for ten years. Suzanne is about to have an upsetting encounter with her aged mother who is in a nursing home. When Suzanne returns home, she shares with John the incident with her mother. The proper response to Suzanne's sharing her hurt is for John to comfort her, but instead, John gives various unproductive responses. Finally, he speaks words of genuine comfort.

Scene

[Suzanne and her mother are at the nursing home.]

> **Suzanne:** Mother, you've got to eat! You can't go on starving yourself to death.
> **Mother:** I'm not hungry.
> **Suzanne:** Mom, don't be difficult. Not only are you not eating, the nursing staff says you've been staying in your room all day by yourself. You need to get out and make some friends.
> **Mother:** That nursing staff has no business watching me like a hawk.
> **Suzanne:** They're not watching you like a hawk. They care about you and want you to be safe and healthy.
> **Mother:** They don't care about me - and neither do you!
> **Suzanne:** Mother! How can you say that?

Mother: It's true.

Suzanne: It is not! I come to see you at least every other day.

Mother: Why not every day?

Suzanne: Mother, I've got three small children at home to take care of; sometimes I just can't get away.

Mother: Like I said, you just don't care.

Suzanne: Mother...

Mother: You go on now... come back when you can.

(Later in the day, Suzanne is at home, sharing with her husband.)

Suzanne: John, I'm so upset. I went by to see mother today. She refuses to eat her meals, she's driving the nursing staff crazy, and when I was about to leave, she accused me of not caring for her.

John: Sweetheart, I've told you before, old people just act like that. I'm sure if you were to take a poll of everyone who has a parent in that nursing home they'd have similar frustrations. You need to face the facts, honey, it's just a part of the cycle of life; parents get old and they need to be taken care of.

Which unproductive response is this?

John: Sweetheart, remember we went through the same ordeal with my parents. I can remember getting so frustrated with my dad that I thought I was going to have to hire a full-time nurse. And my dad wouldn't even go to a nursing home, he insisted on staying in his house. At least at the nursing home they fix meals for your mother, and they're available in case of an emergency. All in all, this is coming at a bad time for me; I'm really busy at the office, and I don't need the extra burden of having to deal with your mom.

Which unproductive response is this?

John: Wow, that's a pretty tough situation. But the whole world doesn't revolve around your mom. Let's not make a big deal about this; it's not the only thing going on in our lives. There's plenty of good things to concentrate on - Jimmy's T-ball game is this afternoon, we're going off together next weekend. Don't let this one event get you down. What did you say was for dinner?

Which unproductive response is this?

John: Suzanne, that's ridiculous. You've been a wonderful daughter to your Mom. No one would ever accuse you of being unloving and uncaring. You're one of the most caring people I know. Don't let it get you down! We've been through tough times before, and you handled them like a champ! I've no doubt that you'll do it again!

Which unproductive response is this?

John: Well, it's time we do something about it. Let's call the nursing home administrator and get her input, I'm sure this is not the first time something like this has happened. We might need to raise a little cain; remember the squeaky wheel gets the oil, and if you want them taking care of her, you're going to have to make some noise. Relative to the meals, believe me, your mother will eat if she gets hungry enough. Perhaps a change in diet would be good.

Which unproductive response is this?

John: That's bad news. We're already paying out the nose for nursing home care. If your mother gets to where she needs a personal nurse, the cost will sky-rocket. How in the world can we do that and send Jill to college? And with all the pressure I'm under at work, I don't need another problem.

Which unproductive response is this?

John: That makes me so mad! Your mother *can* control what she does; she's just doing that to get attention. She needs to realize that she's hurting you by her ridiculous statements. I'm tempted to call her and give her a piece of my mind. And relative to the nursing home's administration - I'll have the state agency down on them so fast, their heads will spin! Which unproductive response is this?

John: Suzanne, I'm really sorry that you had a hurtful encounter with your mom. (John reaches over and holds Suzanne's hand.) It hurts me to see you hurt. I know you love your mom, and it's hard to hear her say things like that. Next time you go to the nursing home, let me go with you, just to give you support.

What makes this response so effective?

_____

_____

Study Question

After completing this exercise, discuss with your spouse, which unproductive response you are most likely to engage in. Then pray together and ask the God of all comfort to use you, on a more consistent basis, to comfort others (2 Corinthians 1:2-4).

_____

_____

Leave Father
and Mother

Phil and Susy's Journey

An explosion took place one morning in the Morris household when Pete told Jackie that he had been having an affair. In the midst of the argument, Pete even blamed his infidelity on Jackie's uncontrollable temper, and further accused her of being insensitive to his needs for attention and physical affection.

Soon after Pete confessed his infidelity, he flew to another city and tried a court case, (and did a fairly good job of it). His callousness and unconcern were evident signs of his hardened heart.

When Jackie first related this experience to me, she asked me not to tell Phil, being afraid it would ruin Pete's Christian witness. But later, with Jackie's permission, I shared with Phil, and the two of us vowed to do our best to reclaim the Morris' marriage. As Phil and I analyzed and prayed over their situation, we were shocked to realize that they both shared the same problem. Their hearts were hardened to their sin. The initial question was—were they willing to repent so that healing could begin?

Although Jackie had come to Christ at an early age, she grew up with deep insecurities and carried a lot of false guilt. As a result, the normal stresses and anxieties of each day quickly filled her emotional cup, at which point her anger would erupt. These outbursts of anger would occur even though she spent time in the Bible every day and faithfully attended Bible studies. Although she was a Christian, the hurt she sustained in childhood was slowly destroying her marriage. She had never completely "left" the pain of her past, so she was not capable of "cleaving" to her husband and becoming "one" with him.

When we first met with Pete, his main problem was an unwillingness to accept responsibility for his sin. He kept blaming Jackie. He not only resented her temper, but in one of our sessions, he confessed his anger with Jackie because she, like her mother, was not able to have children (Jackie had been adopted).

A real breakthrough came for Pete when we shared with him Romans 14:12, *"Each of us will give an account of himself to God."* He finally realized that he alone was responsible for his infidelity and that it was sin in need of confession. When he brought up Jackie's temper problem, 1 Peter 2:20 was our response: *"But how is it to your credit if you receive a beating for doing wrong and endure it? But if you suffer for doing good and you endure it, this is commendable before God."* Finally, they both took responsibility for their own sins and properly confessed.

If we had stopped at this point, their marriage would not have been completely healed. It was obvious that Jackie was really controlled by her past. Previously, Pete's anger and resentment toward Jackie had prevented him from having any empathy for what she had been through—he didn't even care to know. But after the time of confession and forgiveness, Jackie felt that she had a "safe place" in which to share her pain. For the first time in their married life, she sensed that her husband truly cared for her past hurt.

One by one, Jackie began to identify and share the hurtful experiences of her past. It was not a pretty picture. She felt rejected by her father, inadequate with her mother, hurt by her parents' divorce (for which she blamed herself), and envious of other children who were not adopted. All of these issues contributed to Jackie's improper view of God and herself. Her "full cup" produced many symptoms: at a young age, she learned to use her anger to manipulate people; her anxiety produced a fear of failure which led to obsessive tendencies for perfection. She was always trying to change Pete in the same way her mother had tried to change her father and she feared that Pete would reject her because she was childless.

What Jackie shared, broke our hearts. As we imagined her as a small child, experiencing such pain and hurt, our hearts were filled with sorrow.

Amazingly, when Jackie shared with us, it wasn't in anger. She truly grieved her pain and loss. She mourned.

Our response? We comforted her. We didn't try to cheer her up, or explain to her why these things happened. We didn't minimize her pain, or spiritualize her loss, (*"And we know that in all things God works for the good of those who love Him..."* Romans 8:28); we simply comforted her. We *"mourned with those who mourn"* (Romans 12:15). She was particularly blessed watching Pete, perhaps for the first time, understand her past and empathize with her.

Pete's sense of brokenness and repentance was further deepened as he came to better understand his wife. He realized how his infidelity had not only caused present pain, but had served to revisit unhealed pain. Jackie's vulnerability and willingness to expose her deepest needs, in turn, prompted Pete to be more open about his moral failures.

It took several sessions to deal with the most critical issues and in a matter of months, their marriage had experienced a deep level of healing.

In retrospect, we had simply helped Jackie "leave" the pain of her past, so she could "cleave" to her husband. And just as the scripture promises, they were then able to "become one." *"For this reason a man will leave his father and mother and be united to his wife, and they will become one flesh"* (Genesis 2:24).

David and Teresa's Reflections

Yes, marital intimacy will always be elusive if we don't leave our family of origin. And this leaving involves several different areas. To illustrate, let's consider a hypothetical couple named Dave and Laurie and analyze their situation.

Dave and Laurie are having marriage problems. On the surface it appears that their problems are somewhat "normal and predictable"; their symptoms seem to be common problems which plague many couples. Laurie has occasional outbursts of jealousy; Dave responds by defending himself. Dave gets impatient with his wife's less than immaculate house-keeping; Laurie feels frustrated, used, and unappreciated. Rather than face these issues head on, both Dave and Laurie tend to avoid them by escaping into their own activities. When Dave works too many hours at the job, Laurie just goes over to her mom's house and spends the evening talking to her mom and step-dad.

For years they've been refereeing their symptoms but the problems just won't go away. A root issue is feeding the symptoms and until it's properly dealt with, the surface problems may change slightly, but they won't go away.

There are three commands in Genesis 2:24 and the order is important. A husband and wife can't "become one" until they "cleave" to one another and they can't cleave until they've "left" mother and father. Laurie and Dave's problems are rooted in the fact that they've not yet left their family of origin.

Leaving and cleaving involves at least four areas.

1. We must leave certain opinions and expectations about behaviors that we observed in our parents. This is the basis for Dave's misunderstanding regarding Laurie's housecleaning. Dave grew up in a home where "cleanliness was next to godliness." His mom was obsessive about house cleaning. When vacuuming the floor, she wasn't satisfied unless the vacuum cleaner's wheel marks were all parallel. She spent the better part of two days each week cleaning the house.

The problem is, Dave thinks that the cleaning standard his mom adopted for her household should be the criteria by which all others are judged. While his mom's high standards might have been alright for that household, it should not become the norm for his. Laurie is a neat person but isn't fastidious about cleanliness. Besides, she works a full-time job and is actively involved in church and with her kids. At this point in their family's life, keeping the house immaculate just isn't that important. Dave needs to "leave" his opinion and expectation regarding perfect housework.

Study Question

> What expectations might you have brought into marriage which could be hindering your "becoming one"?

_____

_____

2. We must leave certain behaviors that we observed in our family of origin. The behaviors may have worked or not worked but must be left behind if we are to become one. Dave and Laurie both had parents who avoided conflict; they simply escaped into their own activities. For Dave and Laurie to experience healing they will need to leave this unhealthy behavior behind by learning to face the issues and share the truth in love (Ephesians 4:15).

Study Question

> What behavior patterns, either positive or painful might you have brought into marriage with anticipations that "this is the way it should be!"

_____

_____

3. We must no longer look to our family of origin to meet needs that our spouse should meet. This is why Laurie spends an inordinate amount of time at her parent's house. We all have a need for attention and we particularly need our spouse to meet that need. On a regular basis, we need our partner to enter into our world and spend undivided time with us. Dave is neglecting Laurie's need for attention by working too much. But instead of confronting the issue and lovingly talking it out, Laurie is escaping to her family of origin where her need for attention is abundantly met. Her need is legitimate, she's just seeking to have it met in an unhealthy manner. There's nothing wrong with her parents helping to meet certain needs, but they shouldn't be the primary source—that's reserved for her husband.

Study Question

> What "needs" might you still be looking to have met through your family of origin, thus hindering marital giving and oneness?

_____

_____

4. We must "leave" unresolved pain and damaged emotions from our past. When Laurie was twelve years old, her biological father had an extramarital affair. Within a year her parents divorced. Unfortunately, Laurie was caught in the middle of the entire situation. She heard the accusations, felt the anger, and saw the grief. She was hurt, embarrassed, and suspicious and distrustful of men. Although Dave had proven himself to be a "one woman man," Laurie struggled with jealousy. Every time he worked late, went on a business trip, or talked to a woman on the phone, she would ask questions, insinuate accusations, and become emotionally perturbed. The only way for Laurie to be free from her inordinate jealousy is for her to "leave" the pain of her childhood. Consider again the concept of the emotional cup. (See Chapter 4.)

Study Question

What issues of hurt, anger, fear, condemnation or guilt might you have brought into marriage from your growing up years?

_____

_____

John 8:32 states that, *"the truth will set you free."* Have you ever analyzed your marriage relationship, looking for areas in which you have not yet "left" your family of origin? Have you embraced the truth about the four issues mentioned above? As you journey together through the exercises that follow, be open to God's gentle work as the Great Physician.

The Mystery of Leaving, Cleaving and Becoming One

Before there was such a thing as a father and mother, (before Adam and Eve had children), there was a divine command to leave them! The apostle Paul referred to this command as "a great mystery" and even used it to further explain the relationship between Christ and His church (Ephesians 5:31-32). The principles proclaimed in this verse are cloaked with mystery and for every married couple the mystery is both profound and practical. Inherent in the mystery of this verse is a timeless truth for God's three divinely ordained relationships—marriage, family, and the church.

The Mystery of Divine Explanation — "For this Cause"

This divine commandment is preceded by Adam's momentous declaration in Genesis 2:23, *"this is now bone of my bone and flesh of my flesh."* It is for this cause, this reason, that a man will forsake all other human relationships—for the inexpressible joy of committed companionship and the security of mutual love. It is this relationship called "marriage," a part of what Elohim declared as "very good," that prompts this principle of leaving father and mother.

But why prioritize the marriage relationship above the family relationship? Could it be that families will be no stronger and no more divinely-centered than the marital oneness upon which they are built? A healthy family must have as its foundation, a healthy marriage.

> *"My thoughts are not your thoughts, neither are your ways My ways, declares the Lord."*

The marriage relationship portrayed the love affair between Christ and the Church, even before there was a church! He is concerned about our families before they exist and burdened for us to become a Bride to His Son long before His coming. The beauty and complexity of God's provision and foresight underscores the declaration of Isaiah 55:8, *"My thoughts are not your thoughts, neither are your ways My ways, declares the Lord."*

In what ways is the marriage relationship intended to be a model of Christ's relationship with the church?

_____

_____

How might this priority of marriage be a part of God's plan to build strong foundations for families? churches? communities?

_____

_____

The Mystery of Divine Exhortation — "shall a man leave"

There is a divinely declared order here: leave, then cleave, then become one. The significance of this exhortation is reinforced by Jesus during His earthly ministry (Matthew 19:4-6, Mark 10:6-9), and by the apostle Paul (Ephesians 5:31).

To "leave" is to loosen oneself, to prioritize or forsake one relationship for another. It speaks of a certain exclusiveness and is exemplified in the Old Testament when Boaz blessed Ruth over her leaving father and mother to come, *"to a people that you did not previously know"* (Ruth 2:11). The word is used to reassure Israel that Elohim would not fail them or *"forsake them"* (Deuteronomy 31:8).

This progressive and faith-filled journey of "leaving father and mother" will loosen one's soul to truly love and embrace another. The mind will forsake pre-conceived expectations and fantasies of how others and particularly a spouse, must be. Our emotions will be freed from dependent, self-interested love, and the inevitable pain which occurs in a fallen world. Our will is allowed to embrace new behaviors which are right and true for the new relationship of marriage. The inner longing for human intimacy will no longer be directed toward the family of origin but to the new relationship of marriage.

To "cleave" is to be united, to cling together, and it communicates a priority of loyalty. The New Testament speaks of being "joined together" and that mere man should not seek to separate that which has been divinely united (Mark 10:9). This cleaving in marriage portrays the selfless devotion of committed love. What is the origin of such loving loyalty? It is a part of this mystery that we must first cleave to the One who is love (I John 4:16). *"And you have been given fulness in Christ..."* (Colossians 2:10).

To "become one" in marriage is to enjoy a communion of spirit in the things of God, a community of friendship as soul-mates and companions, and a consummation of sexual expression in committed love. It is to bring into unity, two distinct creations of divine worth; God joining them together—spirit, soul, and body (Genesis 2:7).

Study Questions

What areas of "leaving" have you seen effectively working out in your marriage?

_____

_____

In what ways do you feel you and your spouse have effectively worked at "cleaving" together?

_____

_____

During the course of this study, what have been some effective "becoming one" experiences?

_____

_____

The Mystery of Divine Example

Paul's discussion of the mystery of Christ and the church is closely related to this principle of leaving and cleaving. How is it that this verse on "leaving, cleaving, becoming one" speaks to the mystery of Christ and the church?

- Was it not Christ who left His Father? *"Regarding not equality with God a thing to be grasped, but emptied Himself .. becoming obedient to the point of death, even death on a cross"* (Philippians 2:6-8);
- In order that He might cleave to His bride, *"For we have become united with Him"* (Romans 6:5);
- So that we, with Him, might become one, *"But the one who joins himself to the Lord is one Spirit with Him"* (1 Corinthians 6:17).

The mystery of Genesis 2:24 is a profound key to marriage "oneness." Many couples struggle for decades, only to find themselves still dealing with unresolved issues surrounding this principle. God has not left us without instruction. Consider it. Explore it. Experience the truth of it!

Explore A Better Understanding of Your Own Needs

You'll never be any more sensitive to the pain and needs of others than you are to your own! A self-reliant person, claiming to need very little, is most often not very sensitive to others' needs. If you live in denial about your own needs or pain, you may view others as selfish or overly needy. Exploring your own needs might include discussing the following questions with your spouse:

- Complete sentences like, "I feel loved by my spouse when
_____."

- Review a list of intimacy needs to see which three are most meaningful to you as an adult (see Chapter 2). How might the three you picked relate to your growing up?

- Consider which intimacy needs you might have missed to some significant degree from childhood, i.e., "It seems like I missed out on individual attention—time spent just with me doing things I enjoyed."

I think I may have missed _____from my father.

I think I may have missed _____from my mother.

Heal the Pain of Your Unmet Needs

Denial of your own pain will have its effect on your spouse, children and others. Unresolved anger from the past might be displaced upon others. Seeking to minimize or explain away your hurt may keep you insensitive to your spouse's hurt—demanding that he or she respond as you have.

This healing process might include the following

Review the four key intimacy needs listed below, indicating by an "X," needs you clearly missed from both parents, a half-circle "(" for those your father met, an opposing half-circle, ")," for those your mother met and a full circle "○", for those both your mother and father met.

Attention - to take thought of another and convey appropriate interest, concern, and support; to enter into another's world

Approval - to accept as satisfactory; to give formal or official sanction to; to have and express a favorable opinion

Affection - to communicate care and closeness through physical touch and verbalized love.

Comfort - to come alongside with word, feeling and touch; to give consolation with tenderness

Take turns sharing with each other, the hurt that you experienced as a result of these basic intimacy needs not being met in your growing up years. Practice comforting as the hurts are shared; allow your spouse to comfort you. Examples:

- **Attention** - I really missed my father entering my world. *Spouse's response:* That really saddens me; I hurt for you because I love you.

- **Approval** - I never sensed or heard that anyone was proud of me. *Spouse's response:* I deeply regret your not having more approval; it hurts me that you missed it; I'm proud of you and I love you.

- **Affection** - I missed hearing verbalized love from my mother. *Spouse's response:* As I think of you growing up without hearing verbalized love, I feel deep compassion for you.

- **Comfort** - When I experienced hurt and pain growing up, there was seldom anyone there to share my pain with; and when I was able to share my pain, I often just got advice instead of comfort. Spouse's response: It really saddens me that you had to hurt alone. It's so important to be comforted when we're hurting–I'm sorry you missed that.

Begin renewing your mind by replacing lies with God's truth (God says I'm beloved, a saint, a joint-heir, etc.), and the truth that your spouse loves you! Focus on part of the "Divine Mystery of Marriage:"

- You are part of God's plan to restore to your spouse some of the unmet needs from his or her growing up years.
- No other person on planet Earth (over 5 billion people) has been called of God like you have for this divinely ordained role!

Can You Identify Genuine Love?

A Project for a Marriage Staff Meeting and/or family nights.

Read together and discuss 1 Corinthians 13. Each of the questions below may have several good answers but select the most precise illustration to match the questions on love. Discuss how you see your spouse and then other family members demonstrating each one:

_____ 1. How can I show you that I am patient?

_____ 2. How can I show you special kindness?

_____ 3. How can I show you that I am not envious?

_____ 4. How can I show you that I am not trying to impress you?

_____ 5. How can I show you that I am not proud?

_____ 6. How can I show you that you are more important to me than I am to myself?

_____ 7. How can I show you that I am not defensive?

_____ 8. How can I show you that I have erased the memory of an offense?

_____ 9. How can I show you that I am not delighting in your defeats?

_____ 10. How can I show you that I am happy when you make difficult but right decisions?

A. By not reminding you of your past failures.

B. By being helpful to you during sickness and disappointment.

C. By understanding the struggle and praising your standard.

D. By not sharing your defeats with others.

E. By not getting irritated when you don't understand me.

F. By not reacting when you show me that I am wrong.

G. By making your personal needs a priority in my schedule.

H. By not promoting my own skills or accomplishments, but praising the efforts of others.

I. By treating you as I would want myself to be treated.

J. By telling others how God is working through you.

Chapter Eight

Ministering
With a Great
Commandment Heart

Phil and Susy's Journey

It was midnight when Sal called. I immediately knew he was in trouble. "Phil, I need your help. I know you don't practice criminal law, but I need you to get me out of jail. Would you be willing to post bond for me? I don't have my wallet, but if you'll get me out of here, I'll cover you tomorrow when the banks open." Even in a crisis, Sal was calm and businesslike.

Sal was not a distant alcoholic uncle or an unstable homeless man. Sal was chairman of the board, CEO, COO, and CFO of a large company which gave ten percent of its profits to charity. Sal had been driving hard for 30 years, plowing his way to the top. Even as a new believer, he was very active for the Lord– raising funds and charting the course for various Christian ministries. He also established a fund that enabled inner-city children to attend Christian camps.

It saddens me to admit that Sal was my disciple. I had spent over two hundred hours with him, working through *Operation Timothy*. We studied topics like: who Jesus is, how to receive His acceptance and forgiveness, how to gain assurance of eternal life, understanding the Holy Spirit, victory over temptation, and gaining a vision for being salt and light in our world. Sal and I discussed principles of studying the Bible, understanding the value of prayer, choosing a church, developing godly character and discerning God's will and responding in obedience. We had even planned on studying the *Operation Timothy* material on more detailed issues such as ministering in the home and integrating Christian principles in the workplace.

But I never got to know the real Sal. Like a "connect the dots" game, I pushed him from point 1 to 2 to 3 along a prescribed study course; and like good, disciplined businessmen, we never deviated from the plan. But when Sal called that Sunday evening, I realized for the first time that I had failed him.

Because I was never open and vulnerable with Sal, he didn't feel comfortable sharing with me his secret sin. In retrospect, I never revealed to Sal my challenges; I never confided in Sal that Susy and I had struggles in our marriage. Our sharing was surface - superficial - professional. It broke my heart to realize that I had failed my friend, the Lord, and the discipleship process by selfishly protecting my own feelings and weaknesses. Because of my facade, Sal didn't sense that our relationship was a safe place in which he could vulnerably share.

I do remember Sal sharing with me some superficial remarks about having "problems at home," but when the conversation drifted towards emotional issues, I promptly responded with a choice Bible verse. One of my pat answers was to quote Romans 8:28, *"And we know that in all things God works for the good of those who love Him, who have been called according to His purpose."*

So when Sal woke me up that night, I had no clue as to why he was in trouble. My practical mind caused me to simply inquire as to why Angie, his wife, couldn't vouch for him, post bail and get him out of jail. There must have been a mistake.

His response stunned me. With a perfectly calm voice, Sal told me that Angie was at the hospital, being treated for head wounds. For the first time, I realized that I had been meeting weekly for over two years with a man who regularly beat his wife. Because of her love for Sal, Angie had always remained silent about the abuse, but this time Angie's bruised face could not heal in seclusion - she had been knocked unconscious when Sal slammed her against the fireplace hearth.

When Sal asked for my help, I did one of the hardest things I've ever done, and from time to time I still question my decision. Instead of coming to Sal's rescue, I refused to bail him out of jail because I felt that God was dealing with both my dishonesty with Sal and his dishonesty with the Lord.

Eventually, Sal called his operations manager who bailed him out of jail. The incident didn't disrupt his business too much, but it devastated his home life.

After that Sunday night, Sal and I remained cordial and we even saw each other from time to time. But he never wanted to meet with me again or talk about spiritual things. My calls to him were always cut short by a business call that he had to take. Several years later I read in the paper that Sal had been arraigned in a Superior Court for assault and battery. His secret sin was finally public.

Through my experience with Sal, I realized that discipleship requires both the sharing of scriptural truth and the imparting of life. The apostle Paul said it this way, *"We loved you so much that we were delighted to share with you not only the gospel of God but our lives as well, because you had become so dear to us"* (1 Thessalonians 2:8). To be effective, we must seek to fulfill the Great Commission (Matthew 28:19-20) with a Great Commandment heart (Matthew 22:37). In discipleship relationships, imparting truth is critical but not sufficient. We must first love God and others with all our hearts; then we'll be in a position to teach them truth.

David and Teresa's Reflections

It's amazing to think that Phil could have spent so much time with Sal and still not know of his critical marital problems. But to some degree, I'm sure we're all guilty of emphasizing peoples' *knowledge* of Scripture that we ignore whether or not the Scriptures are genuinely impacting their lives. There's a significant difference between imparting truth and imparting life. For effective ministry, you really must do both, and the latter is more difficult and more risky than the former. For relationships to flourish, they need the vulnerable sharing of one's life. Imparting life requires having a Great Commandment love toward others. It is a self-sacrificing, vulnerable type love.

Yes, it's amazing how people can play the game and act like everything's OK when it's not. Here's another story which illustrates the old adage, "You can't tell a book by its cover."

For 30 years Sam has faithfully attended his church. He's one of those "every time the doors are open" members.

His pastor is a renowned Bible expositor. Books, tapes, conferences, radio broadcasts - they are all a part of the "trappings" of his high-profile ministry. He is, in truth, a great teacher, "rightly dividing the word of truth" Sunday by Sunday.

Sam, one of 3,000 church members, has sat in the pew and has listened to his pastor preach at least twice a week, 52 weeks a year, for 30 years. Sam's heard a lot of sermons.

Sam also attends Sunday School. Along with 80 other adults, he sits in the same room Sunday after Sunday listening to a lecture. His teacher is an articulate spokesperson and has been teaching a survey course of the entire Bible for the past eight years. They're currently studying the book of Amos—in particular, the prediction of the dispersion and restoration of Israel and the impending judgments on surrounding nations.

While at church, Sam seems to be doing what's expected of a good church member. He's always there, he cordially (but superficially) relates to others, he even tithes. But at home, Sam is skating on thin ice.

He and his wife have drifted into an unfulfilling, barely tolerable relationship. He brings home the bread and she bakes it, but that's about the extent of their "togetherness." They have both thought about divorce, even threatened a time or two, but know enough Bible to realize that divorce is not a good option. Several years ago, their pastor preached a sermon on Malachi 2:16 and though they did not discuss it, Sam and his wife eliminated divorce as a way to deal with the emptiness and pain of their relationship.

> *Sam is a desperate man, standing on shifting sand.*

Sam's children tend to live their own lives. His lack of relational involvement has forced them to look elsewhere for many of their relational and emotional needs. Fortunately, his daughter has gravitated toward the church youth group. Unfortunately, his son has found companionship with a group of renegades at school. Sam has tried to set and enforce some "spiritual rules" with his children but for some reason they're not properly responding.

Personally, Sam struggles. His anger constantly simmers just below the boiling point; periodically it erupts into outburst. He also struggles with fear, insecurity and selfishness.

When Thoreau said, "Most men live lives of quiet desperation," he was describing Sam. When Jesus described a "foolish man who built his house on sand," He was picturing Sam. Sam is a desperate man, standing on shifting sand.

How can someone so religious be so miserable? How can someone who has heard so much biblical truth be so close to personal and family disaster?

While Sam may mentally know the truth, he is not experiencing it. He has memorized 1 John 4:18, but he's still fearful. He's heard sermons on marriage and family but he doesn't live what he knows.

Who is at fault?

Ultimately, Sam must give an account of himself to God, so the issue stops with him. But secondarily, one has to question a Christian educational philosophy and system in which a student could hear Bible messages for 30 years and yet not demonstrate positive changes in lifestyle or improvement in interpersonal relationships; a system that correctly teaches "what" to believe but inadequately trains its students in "how to" experience what they believe; a system that doesn't provide relational accountability; a system that doesn't encourage relational involvement and intimacy.

Who is at fault?

Romans 14:12 and James 3:11 issue the verdict.

It was passion week and almost a year of opposition from the religious leaders was about to climax at the cross. Throughout the week, Jesus would spend time at the temple during the day and then return to Bethany at night. Perhaps He stayed in the home of His beloved friends Martha, Mary, and Lazarus. Jesus experienced ever increasing opposition in the daylight hours and the caring love of disciples and friends at night. On one day trip, Jesus could no longer tolerate the religious apathy and hypocrisy he saw at the temple and He, *"began driving out those who were buying and selling. He overturned the tables of the money changers and the benches of those selling doves ...and said 'Is it not written: My house will be called a house of prayer for all nations."* As a result, the Scriptures say that, *"the chief priests and teachers of the law began looking for a way to kill Him"* (Mark 11:18).

On another day, recorded in Mark 11:27, the religious leaders, one group at a time, challenged Jesus, trying to trap Him. First, it was the chief priests, scribes and elders who came asking, *"By what authority are you doing these things"* (Mark 11:28)? Then the Pharisees and Herodians challenged Jesus by asking: *"Is it right to pay taxes to Caesar or not"* (Mark 12:14)? And finally the Sadducees, who didn't believe there was a resurrection, invented a story of seven brothers who married the same woman and asked, *"at the resurrection whose wife will she be"* (Mark 12:23)? Each time, Jesus deftly sent his challengers away amazed, astonished, and confounded.

Into that "stump the teacher" atmosphere, a lone scribe appeared. (Scribes taught the law and were experts in it.) The scribe had heard the debating and had seen how well Jesus answered the religious leaders. In a lull in the debate, he stepped up and posed a question to Jesus, *"Of all the commandments, which is the most important"* (Mark 12:28)? Was his question a sincere one? Was he, like the others, trying to "trap the teacher" in His words? Did he just love theological debate? We don't know, but his question was a good one. Jewish rabbis counted 613 individual statutes of the law and constantly tried to differentiate which were "heavy" and which were "light"—which were the most important and which were not as important.

Without hesitation, Jesus answered, *"The most important one is this: 'Hear, O Israel, the Lord our God is one. Love the Lord your God with all your heart and with all your soul and with all your mind and with all your strength.' The second is this: 'Love your neighbor as yourself.' There is no commandment greater than these"* (Mark 12:29-31).

Where did Jesus find these commandments? Where did they appear originally? The first part of Jesus' answer came from Deuteronomy 6:4-6, verses that are known as the "shema," the Hebrew word for "hear." Even today the "shema" is the call to worship in synagogue services. Two thoughts are intriguing: Why did Jesus bypass the "big 10," the Ten Commandments given in the book of Exodus? Were not the Ten Commandments the very "core" of the law and God's first written communication to His people Israel after they came out of bondage in Egypt? Secondly, the setting for the book of Deuteronomy provides an interesting insight. Deuteronomy is a sermon to a whole different generation of people than those who came out of Egypt and who had received the Ten Commandments. Because of the people's disobedience, God caused them to wander in the wilderness for 40 years—long enough for all but two, Joshua and Caleb, to die. Deuteronomy was spoken by Moses to those born in the wilderness wandering. Was God stressing to this second generation what their parents lacked?

Why did Jesus bypass the "big 10," the Ten Commandments given in the book of Exodus?

The second part of Jesus' answer came from the book of Leviticus, a book written to the first generation that came out of Egypt. What's interesting about this aspect of the "great commandment" is its location—Leviticus 19:18: *"Do not seek revenge or bear a grudge against one of your people, but love your neighbor as yourself."* If X generally marks the spot for treasure, who would have thought that treasure was buried in Leviticus 19. Why did Jesus find treasure in this particular verse? Why did Jesus pull together two commandments spoken to two different generations and call them the "Great Commandment?"

A Message to Empower the Church

It's the "Great Commandment" heart which empowered the first century church. To read the first chapters of Acts, it is clear that they were loving God with all that they were and were loving their neighbor as themselves:

"They devoted themselves to the apostles' teaching and to the fellowship, to the breaking of bread and to prayer. Everyone was filled with awe, and many wonders and miraculous signs were done by the apostles. All the believers were together and had everything in common. Selling their possessions and goods, they gave to anyone as he had need. Every day they continued to meet together in the temple courts. They broke bread in their homes and ate together with glad and sincere hearts, praising God and enjoying the favor of all the people. And the Lord added to their number daily those who were being saved" (Acts 2:42-47).

We find similar encouragement from the Epistles. Romans 13:9, 10 restates the fact that every other commandment may be summed up in one rule: *"Love your neighbor as yourself...and love is the fulfillment of the law."* Other verses similarly focus in on "love:" Hebrews 13:1, Galatians 5:13, and 1 Corinthians 13. John's burdened appeal to the church at Ephesus was *"that they had left their first love"* (Revelation 2:4). And in light of Matthew's end time prediction *"because of the increase in wickedness, the love of most will grow cold"* (Matthew 24:12), the challenge to minister from a Great Commandment Heart may represent, for God's people, the great crisis of the 20th century church and the great challenge and opportunity for the 21st century church.

Ingredients of a Great Commandment Heart

A Great Commandment heart pursues intimacy with God and with others. Significantly, Christ's great commandment spoke both of a vertical relationship with God and a horizontal relationship with others. Two commandments became the "Great Commandment" because the two are inextricably related. John wrote *"If anyone says, 'I love God,' yet hates his brother, he is a liar. For anyone who does not love his brother, whom he has seen, cannot love God, whom he has not seen"* (1 John 4:20). Jesus taught this in the parable of the Good Samaritan. Enjoying eternal life involves "loving God" and "loving your neighbor" and Jesus taught that a neighbor was anyone in need.

How does a Great Commandment heart pursue intimacy with God and others? Intimacy is pursued through relational experience based on truth. Significantly, Christ's great commandment spoke of relationships and not rules. Why not keep the Ten Commandments or some of the other countless rules? Christ's answer seems to say, "truly know and love the One behind the rules and everything else is easy; it's My constraining love that empowers righteous living." Christ's earthly ministry role-models to us what "loving others" looks like as His focus is on relating to others in love, not keeping external rules. Jesus, when challenged by the Pharisees about why His disciples were picking grain on the Sabbath (working), responded that *"the Sabbath was made for man, not man for the Sabbath"* (Mark 2:27). Compassion for people was to be at the heart of true religion. When we focus on the external rules, internal love is quenched. Empowered by His Spirit and equipped in His word, the church becomes equipped to experience love with God and others.

And why does a Great Commandment heart pursue intimacy with God and others? Because God has made provision for both our aloneness and fallenness. Only love satisfies both human dilemmas. It's love, portrayed at Calvary, that satisfies the penalty for our sin; and it's the God who is love who makes provision for sin so that we can lovingly relate to Him, removing our aloneness. It's as if Christ would say to the scribe, "It's love that satisfies all other rules."

"We love because He first loved us" (1 John 4:19). There is no greater demonstration of this "provision" for aloneness and fallenness than to explore the question—Where does the love come from that we might love God and others? The love comes from God! Just stop and imagine, we have a God who gives us the Great Commandment and then gives us His love to fulfill it!

Experiencing Great Commandment Love in Marriage

So how does this relate to marriage? Could it be that marriage is part of God's plan for you and me to learn to love just one person, and then a few others called children (family) and a few more in our witness and discipleship? Perhaps marriage is a "laboratory" in which we can learn to live selflessly and vulnerably with others. Perhaps it is in marriage that we experience a true "imparting of our life" to another person. Maybe it is in the marriage relationship that we can learn to experience confession, forgiveness, comfort, and speaking the truth in love.

It has been our hope that these marriage principles have been an encouragement to your marriage and that they have helped equip you to fulfill the Great Commission with a Great Commandment love.

Grace:
Enabling Intimacy

Intimacy is often defined as, "genuinely knowing another person, and becoming caringly involved in their life as we allow them to know us in a similar way." Additionally, we can identify various "intimacy needs" such as acceptance, attention, affection, appreciation, and comfort. But there must be a "power" outside ourselves that enables the real experiencing of intimacy.

The complexity and overwhelming "neediness" of our human condition means that relationships tend to move toward deterioration. It's what happens when two humanly "bankrupt" partners join forces together in marriage. It's what has been described as each partner becoming like a "tick" on a dog—"I'm here to take from you." —only to find in such a marriage that we have two ticks and no dog! Our only hope is outside ourselves and this "closed system" of humanism. An unlimited source of love, acceptance, comfort, and forgiveness is needed to enable and sustain an intimate relationship. Such a source is available, and His name is Jesus. The Bible calls this divine contribution…grace!

> *"As good stewards of the manifold grace of God"* (I Peter 4:10).

Grace Initiates

Divine grace initiates our intimate relationship with God. It was Christ who humbled Himself, took on the form of a servant and became obedient to the point of death (Philippians 2:7-10)…that we might become a partaker of the divine nature (2 Peter 1:4). Noted Bible scholar Donald Barnhouse speaks of our undeserved gift of grace in this way "love that goes upward is worship; love that goes outward is affection; love that stoops is grace." Christ "stooped" from heaven, entered into my world and gave Himself! What an example! Having partaken of this divine initiative, one spouse initiates caring involvement in a partner's life and it's this initiative that genuinely communicates, "I was thinking of you," and "I care." In a similar way, parents can take initiative to really know their children as good stewards of this divine grace.

Grace Liberates

It's also grace that frees us from the penalty of sin and grants us eternal life so that one day we will be free from the presence of sin (Titus 3:5). But "much more" than this, it's grace that can liberate us from the power of sin in this life.

- There's liberty from selfishness...freeing me to see and give to the needs of others.
- There's liberty from criticism...freeing me from judging others.

Just as Christ looked beyond my faults and saw my needs, I'm now free to look beyond others' faults and see their needs. Instead of judging another's behavior, we have the freedom to give unselfishly in meeting their intimacy needs (Philippians 2:3).

> *I'm now free to look beyond others' faults and see their needs.*

Study Question

List areas of personal liberty that you've experienced during this study...

_____

_____

Grace Motivates

Living in the awe and wonder of all that we have and are in Christ—motivates a stewardship of grace.

This life of intimacy with God and others is not lived out in obligation or duty. There wells up within the believer such a joyful gratefulness and humble appreciation that giving unconditionally to a spouse, child, friend or even our enemy is uncontrollable! Out of our innermost being will flow rivers of living water that nourish intimacy in human relationships (John 7:38). Grace is infectious, contagious...the love of Christ is now "constraining" us (2 Corinthians 5:14).

Study Question

List areas of "giving and loving" in your marriage where you have experienced additional motivation during this study.

_____

_____

Grace Lubricates

Charles Swindoll, in *The Grace Awakening*, speaks of the marriage "oiled by grace." It's grace that lubricates the inevitable "rough edges" of our humanness. The demands and "closeness" of marriage and family inevitably bring the human rough spots to the surface...but the "intimate" relationship ministers the oil of God's grace:

- As acceptance is granted...in spite of "performance" (Romans 15:7).
- As edifying words are shared to build-up and encourage (Ephesians 4:29).
- As personal responsibility is emphasized in focusing on our walk with our Savior (Romans 14:10-12).

As we experience God's grace in relationships—we come to enjoy more of an "abundance," the kind that's exceeding, beyond what we could ask or think (John 10:10, Ephesians 3:20).

> *It's grace that lubricates the inevitable "rough edges" of our humanness.*

Study Question

What other blessings of abundance have you experienced during this study with your spouse?

_____

_____

Journal of Gratefulness— Psalm 103:2

"Forget None of His Benefits"

The Benefits of Gratefulness

Multiplied blessings are ours as we pause to "forget none of His benefits" toward us (Psalm 103:2). Among the numerous benefits of a grateful heart are the following:

- Gratefulness guards us from a critical, negative attitude.
- Gratefulness guards us from a judgmental spirit.
- Gratefulness, when expressed to others, can motivate them to continue in "good deeds."
- Gratefulness, when acknowledged to God, is an important element of worship.

The Search for Blessings

Take time this week to identify "blessings" you've experienced during this study; consider how you've been blessed through your spouse, other group members.

Additionally, you might regularly involve family members in a "blessing search" as each member shares a recent blessing and assumes responsibility for express appreciation. Where to "look:"

- Loved ones, who you've recently been reminded of in a special way.
- Character qualities in spouse, family or friends which are challenging.
- Often over-looked blessings of life, health, provision and creation.
- Specific answers to prayer.
- Spiritual realities like the Scriptures, salvation, Holy Spirit, grace, and comfort.

The Expression of Appreciation

Appreciation helps seal in our hearts the reality of our blessings and when we express appreciation, others are blessed and encouraged. Appreciation can be shared:

- Verbally, with a simple "thanks."
- In writing, with a note of appreciation.
- Publicly, as testimony is given of our genuine gratitude

Our verbal thanks and testimony to others are of major importance.

How We Have Been Blessed

…look for God's interventions, expressions of family member love, answered prayers and special people, events and happenings

How We Shared Our Appreciation

…say thanks, write a note, take a gift, give testimony

Partnership Follow-up Plan

To help keep your "Unlimited Partnership" healthy consider completing the following list of "intimate encounters." To help you better identify the type of "intimate encounters" you and your spouse enjoy, check the items you think would most appeal to your mate. Then compare lists and design a follow-up plan to address each of the encounters!

Mate	Myself	
☐	☐	Holding hands
☐	☐	Going for a walk
☐	☐	An unexpected hug
☐	☐	Finding a love note
☐	☐	Receiving a surprise gift
☐	☐	Being served a favorite meal
☐	☐	Being told "I love you"
☐	☐	Helping with the kids
☐	☐	Being approached sexually
☐	☐	Seeing the house straight
☐	☐	Seeing the lawn looking nice

☐	☐	Receiving compliments on looks
☐	☐	Taking a shower together
☐	☐	A surprise "date"
☐	☐	Getting a back rub or massage
☐	☐	Having dinner out
☐	☐	Being praised for achievements
☐	☐	Having a quiet conversation

Marriage Staff Meeting
Discussion Questions

The next time you have a Marriage Staff Meeting, use these questions as a catalyst for good conversation.

1. If I were to describe my marriage after this study with one word, the word I would use is...
2. What word do you think your spouse would use to describe your marriage?
3. What benefits are you receiving from your marriage relationship that you wouldn't have received if you had remained single. Be very specific.
4. What strengths have you seen in your spouse during this study? How will you express your awareness?
5. What, during this study, has your spouse done that made you feel particularly loved or of value?
6. What do you plan to do to better express your love and appreciation toward your spouse?
7. What additional efforts toward intimacy have you seen your spouse making? How have you expressed gratefulness?
8. What are some of your present goals for your marriage? What can you do differently that will enable you to reach them?

Here are some suggestions on what answers to number 8 might look like:

- I will show more of an interest in my spouse's activities by asking questions.
- I will spend more time thinking about positive factors in my marriage relationship and attempt to discover ways to be what my spouse wants and needs.
- I will take time to pray for and with my family, especially my spouse.
- If I have any resentments against family members - and particularly my spouse - I will forgive them now.

CBMC of USA
Ministry Resources

To assist in the process of personal spiritual growth, evangelism and discipleship, CBMC of USA provides these ministry tools and resources.

Evangelism and Discipleship

- **Living Proof 1: Evangelism As a Lifestyle**—This 12-part video training series dramatically portrays the challenges and joys of building friendships with non-Christians, allowing them to observe our lives and begin to understand what it means to be a follower of Christ. This series is especially effective for use in small groups.
- **Living Proof 2: Lifestyle Discipleship**—This sequel to *Living Proof* is also presented in 12 sessions and takes the material a step further, showing the opportunity and difficulties new believers encounter in their desire to become faithful, consistent and growing followers of Christ and disciplemakers.
- **Brave, Strong and Tender**—by Phil Downer and Chip MacGregor. This is a powerful, personal and practical call for men and couples to leave their foxholes and engage in the spiritual battle that surrounds them - to find victory in their homes, businesses, communities and their world. The book is not only an encouragement to walk closely with Christ, but also to reach others with His love and train them to be disciplemakers. (Includes study guide for small group discussion.)
- **First Steps**—This one-book introductory Bible discussion guide helps seeking non-Christians and new believers begin to understand the central truths of the Bible, the person and work of Jesus Christ, and how to attain eternal life.
- **Operation Timothy**—This series, now available in a revised and updated version, has been used to nurture and equip thousands of new believers. It starts with the basics of the Christian faith and then proceeds to address important issues of

personal discipleship.

- **Leadership and Ministry Development Series**—This series has been created to communicate the process of developing a personal and team ministry that will continue bearing fruit as team members demonstrate a devotion to Jesus Christ, to one another and to the Gospel.

Marriage and Family

- **Family Conferences and Couples Retreats**—Throughout the year, CBMC sponsors dozens of these events designed to help men, women, and children deepen their relationship to God, one another, and to grow their understanding and skill in how to effectively minister to others.
- **Fanning the Flame**—This thought-provoking, biblically based discussion series is designed to help men learn how to better understand, love and cherish their wives in the ways God intended.
- **Marriage Intimacy Groups**—Couples meet in small groups, focusing on and evaluating their marriages in light of the principles contained in the books, *Unlimited Partnership* and *Intimate Encounters*, with the goal of having a growing and cherishing marriage relationship.

Business and Work

- **Forums**—These are small teams of business owners and executives who meet monthly to provide counsel, mutual encouragement and accountability in their desire to learn how to effectively integrate Biblical principles in running their companies.
- **Contact Quarterly**—This high-quality, colorful quarterly magazine uses features and practical articles to help Christians in business discover how to practically integrate biblical principles where they work and live.
- **Jesus Works Here and The complete Christian Businessman**—Both edited by Robert J. Tamasy, these books offer concise but persuasive accounts of how business people have learned o put biblical principles into action in the work-

place and the neighborhood.

- **Margin**—This provocative discussion series examines the many demands of contemporary life and shows how to achieve an abundant life, filled with the blessings of God, in an overloaded world.

- **The Gospel and the Briefcase**—by Ted DeMoss and Robert J. Tamasy. This is a story of what God can do through people who are willing to be used to make an eternal difference in the lives of people they meet, on the job and in their communities.

For more information about a **CBMC** group in your area, or how to obtain any of these resources, write or call CBMC of USA, 1800 McCallie Avenue, Chattanooga, TN 37404 • 800.566.2262

Intimate Life
Ministries -
Resources and Training

Intimate Life Ministries is a resource and training ministry, helping build Healthy Churches for the 21st century. Here is a brief description of several major resources and information regarding a training opportunity.

Resources

- **Intimate Encounters** *by Ferguson & Thurman* — (273 Pages) 16 chapters focusing on subjects such as Intimacy needs, childhood and marital hurts, and goal setting. A practical guide to the secrets of a great marriage. Can be used in classes or small groups.
- **Intimate Encounters Audio Tape Set** *by David & Teresa Ferguson*— 8 audio tapes focusing on the 16 chapters of the Intimate Encounters workbook in 20-25 minute segments. The tapes can be used for leader preparation, or for individual couples to use while going through the workbook.
- **Top 10 Intimacy Needs booklet** *by Ferguson and McMinn* — (76 pages) Good for ladies', men's, singles or couples classes to introduce the biblical principles of intimacy.
- **Parenting With Intimacy** *by Ferguson, Warren and Ferguson*— (232 pages) Discover the journey of parenting as an exciting, dynamic investment of yourself in your children as "gifts" from the Lord.
- **Parenting With Intimacy Workbook** *by Ferguson, Warren, & Ferguson* —(385 pages) With the help of exercises, activities, checklists and personal inventories, you will have a guide for understanding your child's needs and your own and how to meet those needs.
- **Intimate Family Moments** *Devotional by Ferguson, Warren & Ferguson* —(345 pages) With the use of Scripture, Bible dramas, discussion starters and activities, you can experience biblical principles together as a family. There are lessons for everyone - ages 4-99.

- **Intimate Life Newsletter**—This monthly publication is a helpful source of new and expanded Intimate Life topics. Practical and easy to read, the newsletter can help keep your relationships fresh and vital.

Leadership Institute

An Intimate Life Leadership Institute is an intensive, four day training course offered by Intimate Life Ministries. During the Institute, participants will receive thorough training in Intimate Life principles and learn how these principles can be applied to local church ministries, community based ministry and para-church organizations.

The purpose of the Institute is to impart the Intimate Life message to the participants such that:
- Intimacy becomes a lifestyle, both in personal relationships and ministry.
- The Intimacy message can be specifically taught and shared in every segment of ministry.